Time for Tapioca

Time for Tapioca

BY CHARLOTTE STRYKER

NEW YORK : THOMAS Y. CROWELL COMPANY

ON our first day in Java we were aroused by loud knocking on our bedroom doors. As it was still dark, we all jumped out of bed, thinking that the house must be on fire. Then we realized that we were not still at home in Roselawn, Pennsylvania, but on an island at the other side of the world. Perhaps it wasn't a fire but an earthquake or volcanic eruption.

A faint light showed in the hall and everyone rushed to his door—Dad and Mother, my four young brothers, and I—still dazed with sleep but thoroughly alarmed.

Our Dutch housekeeper, Juffrouw Gelder, stood in the hall, wide awake and quite calm. "He is half past five," she said in her quaint English. "Usually one rises at five o'clock himself. But I let you sleep longer. I thought you must be tired after your long journey."

"Tired? I'm dead!" Dad snorted. "And I intend to sleep for several hours more." He turned on his heel and closed his door with a loud bang.

Mother in her mild voice said: "It really is a *little* too early. We generally get up at seven-thirty . . ."

"Yes, perhaps in America," Juffrouw Gelder broke in. "But here in Java one rises at five. It is a custom of the country."

"All the same, it's really a *little* too early," Mother gently insisted as she turned to her room.

But Juffrouw Gelder had crossed her arms on her meager bosom and was staring hard at Mother. A waspish little spinster of fifty, Juffrouw's small gray eyes were as sharp as needles and Mother paused with her hand on the doorknob.

She had never employed a housekeeper before and had, as a matter of fact, gotten along very well without one. But now she was a stranger in a strange land. She had a big, unfamiliar house on her hands and Javanese servants who spoke only Malay. She felt herself very dependent on Juffrouw Gelder and on Juffrouw's English, peculiar though it was. Perhaps, as the Dutch-woman suggested, we should fall in with the customs of the country. Then too, Juffrouw's sharp eyes were very compelling and Mother, besides being mild, was somewhat easily intimidated.

"Very well, since the children are awake anyway . . ."

They were awake and very wide awake. We had docked in Batavia late the previous evening and had not reached our new home until half past eleven at night. But this morning the boys had been awakened expecting something exciting. They had gotten over their disappointment but definitely didn't want to go back to bed. They wanted to explore the premises.

Jim and Peter, the two oldest, had already rushed down the hall and out onto the back porch where an open door showed the first faint traces of dawn. The younger ones, Frank and Henry, had taken off in the

2

opposite direction toward the living room where they had spied a parrot on a perch. From the screams and squawks, we could hear that the small boys and the bird were already engaged in battle.

"Boys must not tease parrot," said Juffrouw. "And must also not leave house in pajamas. It is not proper." She hesitated a moment as to which impropriety she should deal with first, then went off toward the porch after Jim and Peter.

"Isn't she wonderful, Charlotte?" said Mother in a dazed tone. "She's not only going to manage all of those servants but she seems to want to look after the children as well."

"And she gets us up at five-thirty in the morning!" I added. "What are we supposed to do now?"

Mother didn't know exactly but she suggested that we put on our bathrobes and take a look around the house. On our arrival we had had only a confused impression of a great many immense rooms with gleaming tile floors. Also, though it was dark, we realized that the house had extensive grounds because we had followed the driveway for a considerable distance from the street to the imposing, white-columned front porch.

When the car halted, Mother had exclaimed that it was simply lovely, it reminded her of Mount Vernon! Then Dad had turned to our Dutch friend, Mijnheer Verstoffen, who was at the wheel. Dad again thanked the jolly Dutchman for all he had done for us, meeting us at the dock with his car and renting a house complete with servants and a housekeeper. But, Dad asked,

3

a little hoarsely, how much would it all cost? Mijnheer Verstoffen told him the amount in guilders. Dad was not yet familiar enough with guilders to be able to figure it out in dollars. Anyhow, the hour was near midnight and there we were, all seven of us, and behind us was a taxi piled with our thirty-one pieces of hand luggage.

Last night the house had seemed awfully big. And in the early morning light it looked bigger than ever to Mother and me as we stood in the vast living room. Mother looked very pretty in her kimono with her curly, dark hair loosely pinned up, but also very small and lost.

And no wonder. The room was about twenty by forty and had a fifteen-foot ceiling. In the center of the bare, shining floor was a velvet-draped table overhung by a large, green silk lampshade. An old-fashioned mahogany parlor set was formally arranged around the table. But the corners of the room were empty except for some lonely-looking potted plants. On one wall was a large, gilt-framed portrait of the Queen of the Netherlands.

"Nice-looking woman, isn't she?" said Mother politely. Then to Frank and Henry, who were still battling with the parrot, she said, "If you don't stop teasing that poor bird I hope he bites you."

"We wasn't," said Henry promptly. He turned to Mother with his big, innocent, blue eyes. In her five years with little Henry Mother still hadn't learned that her youngest and perhaps dearest son could look her right in the eye and lie like a trooper.

Frank, who was six, had only ordinary brown hair

and gray eyes but he was more truthful. "We *were* teasing him but just to see if parrots can really talk."

The tall door at the end of the room burst open and the two older boys rushed in from the front porch. Jim was a tall, skinny lad of twelve. Peter, two years younger, was short and pudgy. He was further distinguished by a shock of straight hair which Mother complained always looked like hay. The older boys were still barefoot and in their pajamas. Apparently Juffrouw Gelder had not been able to catch them.

"We don't like it here," they exclaimed. "We don't like it at all. You said there were jungles and volcanoes and wild animals and everything. But we've been all over the place. Out in our yard and we looked at the other yards and houses around here and it's just like Roselawn. It's not what we thought it would be like at all."

It wasn't what Mother had thought it would be either. She had seen that Java was a little dot on the map halfway around the world from Roselawn. That had led her to imagine it as a small, tropic isle with some white sand, palm trees, and a few brown natives. But Dad didn't use his imagination about such things, he got the facts, all the facts, and he got them straight.

He told Mother that Java wouldn't be a dot when we got there because it was the size of the state of New York. Also, there were not only a few brown natives but nearly fifty million of them. True, there *were* palm trees but vast rubber, tea, coffee, and sugar plantations as well. Java, the most important island of the Dutch East

Indies, was well populated with Hollanders and there were railroads, large modern towns, and almost everything we had at home.

But Mother wasn't impressed with facts; they just went in one ear and out the other. She persisted in her own idea of Java as a tiny island with only sand and palm trees. That was why, besides our thirty-one pieces of hand luggage and our car, we had brought seven immense crates of canned goods, five large trunks of clothing, a first-aid kit complete with antisnake serum, and a dozen bottles of cod liver oil.

"I guess your father was right, as usual," Mother admitted now as she sank back onto the blue satin cushions of the parlor sofa. "But, somehow, I wish—"

Like the boys, Mother perhaps wished that, having made such a long journey, we had come to a place which was a little less like home. At fourteen, I already shared her romantic feelings. I too had expected to find a golden strand where we would live in a picturesque hut under the nodding palms.

"I certainly didn't expect anything like this house," said Mother, glancing from the potted plants in red porcelain jars to the portrait of Queen Wilhelmina in her crown and diamonds. "That Mijnheer Verstoffen was very kind to go to all the trouble of getting it for us but—" She paused.

Mijnheer Verstoffen had been very kind, of course. Still Dad had only written asking him to get us some rooms in a hotel—not a tremendous mansion. Yes, big, jovial Mijnheer Verstoffen had taken a great deal upon himself, what with the house, the servants, and also Juffrouw Gelder who, though only a bit of a thing, seemed rather overpowering. For, besides being house-keeper and taking over the role of nurse, she even told us when to get up in the morning.

But now, having gotten us up, she didn't leave us long to our own devices. She soon appeared in the doorway and announced that it was time for us to take our baths. The ormolu clock which hung opposite Queen Wilhelmina showed it to be only quarter past six—rather early for baths. But we all followed Juffrouw's orders to go to our rooms and get our soap, towels, and wash-cloths. We were intrigued about where we would bathe because our palatial establishment had no plumbing—only washstands and chamber pots in the bedrooms.

As Juffrouw led us down the hall and out to the back porch I remembered stories I had read about explorers in Africa or somewhere who built a shed in the yard where they rigged up a makeshift shower.

But our yard didn't look like the place for a shed or makeshift. A stretch of velvet lawn under big trees sloped a considerable distance to a low, white building set at right angles to the house. The low building, Juffrouw told us, was called the kampong. It contained the serv-ants' quarters, storerooms, the kitchen and, surprisingly, the bathroom.

The kampong was connected with the back porch by a long, covered walk down which we followed Juffrouw like soldiers on parade. Under the kampong porch were a great many doors, one of which was marked *bad*. We were intrigued about what might be inside *bad* and were still more intrigued when Juffrouw threw open the door on a small, empty room.

"I thought perhaps *bad* is Dutch for 'bath,'" said Mother.

"So it is," said Juffrouw, "and here is the bath."

She pointed to a large cement cistern in one corner of the room.

"You mean that's the tub?"

Whatever it was—*bad*, tub, or bath—the cistern was about three feet high and five feet square. It was big enough for all of us to get into at once but Juffrouw said "no." Apparently one didn't get into the cistern but stood beside it and poured water over oneself with a small bucket.

I took my bath first and it was fun. The boys had fun too. They all went in together and spent three-quarters of an hour throwing water at each other and yelling and screaming. Mother got tired waiting for her turn and went back to her room where she washed at the basin.

After we were dressed, we all trooped into the dining room, feeling pretty hungry. But the fifteen-foot table, though impressive, was bare except for a bowl of artificial flowers on a crocheted mat. We were glad to hear a bell ringing somewhere and followed the sound hopefully. It led us to the back lawn where Juffrouw was seated at a table under a tree. We took our places beside her and were soon joined by Dad who, long and lanky, came striding across the grass. He was sort of grouchy because it was still only seven o'clock.

The lawn, enclosed by the house, the kampong, and the covered walk, formed a tree-shaded courtyard of emerald green sward edged with flower beds. Purple passion flowers entwined with orange and yellow flame vines sprawled over the walls and porches. Under the porch eaves hung sprays of orchids and among the orchids were cages of bright-colored parakeets which chattered as their cages shifted in the light breeze.

It was the most delightful spot imaginable for breakfast but, though the table was set, there was no breakfast until Juffrouw rang her silver bell again. Then there was a bright flash under the kampong porch and a servant appeared, bearing a tray.

On our arrival we had seen the servants, at least a dozen of them, lined up at the front door to greet us. But they hadn't greeted us, they merely stood staring blankly before them. Since all wore long skirts, it was difficult to tell which were men and which were women. We hadn't had much time to find out because they had rushed to the taxi for our luggage, rushed into the bedrooms and unpacked, then rushed out of the house and into the night.

Now we saw that the long-skirted person approaching was a man in a white duck jacket and a gaily flowered turban that matched his skirt. Apart from his jacket he was so exotic that we expected him to set down a meal of hummingbirds' tongues or something equally intriguing. But he laid out a good, ordinary American breakfast of ham and eggs, toast and coffee, and orange juice.

While we tucked away a hearty meal, Juffrouw drank

only a cup of tea. Mother told Juffrouw she must be sure to have whatever she liked for breakfast. Perhaps she preferred a Dutch breakfast to an American one. Juffrouw replied that *this* was a usual Dutch breakfast— the first part of it.

As soon as the dishes had been cleared away, the second course was set upon the table. There were platters of cold meat, pickled fish, several sorts of cheese, olives, pickles, and beer. Apparently this was the part of breakfast Juffrouw liked. With delicately crooked little finger she took up a pickled herring sandwich. With the other hand also with crooked finger, she took a pull from her stein of beer.

As Juffrouw had politely sat through our breakfast, we politely sat through hers. That is, Mother and Dad and I did. By the time Juffrouw had gotten to her sixth sandwich and third stein of beer, the boys couldn't sit still any longer and had gone off to continue their investigation of our new home.

It looked as though we wouldn't have to sit still much longer either because Juffrouw was just finishing, when Mijnheer Verstoffen appeared among the flame and passion flowers on the back porch. Last night I had had an impression merely of a big, jolly man. By daylight, Mijnheer Verstoffen was a perfect example of a plump, rosy baby complete with golden curls, bright blue eyes, and all. But he was a baby on a gigantic scale. When Dad, six feet tall and pretty sturdy, stood up to greet him, he looked like a mere lightweight beside the enormous Dutchman.

Verstoffen refused breakfast. But he said he would take just a snack. This proved to be three beers and four sandwiches. We decided that big appetites were a Dutch characteristic. Tiny Juffrouw and tremendous Verstoffen seemed equally hearty eaters.

Finally Verstoffen was ready to take Dad down to the port and help him get our crates, trunks, and car through customs. Dad figured it wouldn't take him more than an hour or so to do that.

"And then," he said with a grin, "time for tapioca!"

He wasn't looking forward to something else to eat but to the business that had brought him to Java in the first place. Dad had had tapioca on his mind for years—not as material for pudding but for glue. His firm, the Roselawn Glue Company of Pennsylvania, didn't make their glue from dead horses as most people did back in 1927. They made it from tapioca which was imported from Java. Dad had decided he could get tapioca cheaper by going to Java and producing it himself instead of buying it from others.

Mijnheer Verstoffen didn't agree with Dad on that point. But then, why should he? He was the man from whom Dad had been buying tapioca. Verstoffen didn't raise the stuff himself but bought it up from many small producers. A lot of small producers producing tapioca was inefficient, Dad thought. What he planned to do was to buy a great big plantation and raise tapioca on a large scale. Then he would build a large, modern factory to process it and the Roselawn Glue Company would get the best quality tapioca flour that could be made. Also, in the long run it would be a lot cheaper.

Verstoffen said that small-scale production was the way tapioca was turned out in Java. It was a custom of the country.

We had heard about the customs of the country from Juffrouw Gelder. They were all right in regard to getting up early, bathing at a cistern, and eating a breakfast the size of a Thanksgiving dinner. But Dad didn't intend to follow them in regard to his tapioca project. He was an American, a businessman, and he was in a hurry. That was why, apart from the expense, he had been sorry that Verstoffen had rented us a house. Because we wouldn't be in Batavia more than a month. It couldn't take longer than that, Dad was sure, for him to buy a plantation and start to work.

2

AFTER Dad had left—and he insisted on driving himself as Verstoffen drove too slowly—Juffrouw took Mother in hand to initiate her into the customs of a Dutch housewife. After breakfast, it seemed, one interviewed the servants.

This ceremony took place in the dining room where Juffrouw, Mother, and I seated ourselves at the long, mahogany table. Then Juffrouw tinkled her little silver bell which she carried with her. Immediately, as if by magic, all the servants filed into the room and lined up, the men in one row and the women in another.

Now Mother and I had a chance to observe them closely and decide which were which. All were in long skirts, or sarongs, but the men wore white jackets while the women had on cotton shirtwaists. The men were turbaned so that only their ears showed; the women's straight, black hair was worn in a knot on the nape of the neck.

They were all small, slightly built, with coffee-colored skins and slanted black eyes. And all stood completely motionless and impassive.

"This is the butler," said Juffrouw, indicating the man who stood nearest her.

"Goodness!" said Mother, impressed.

Juffrouw explained that he waited on the table but he did *not* take charge of the food supplies because "the native," as she called them, couldn't be trusted. The native steals. All of the food was kept in the godown, or storeroom, out in the kampong. So Juffrouw carried the godown key in her pocket and doled out the food required for each meal.

Apropos of food, Mother told Juffrouw about the crates of canned goods and other things we had brought from home. Mother said we certainly wouldn't need them here in Batavia but we probably would when we got on our plantation. Juffrouw replied that there was plenty to eat even on the plantations. But, nevertheless, she was interested in hearing about American foods. Mother said we had brought cereals, principally corn flakes which the boys loved, as well as other things she thought we couldn't get in Java such as tuna fish, sardines, canned sweet potatoes, corn, and other vegetables and fruits.

Meanwhile the butler, a dignified, middle-aged man, stood waiting patiently until Juffrouw turned to him and said that he was *Jongens Sato*. I wasn't used to butlers so I asked Juffrouw if we should call him by his first or his last name. Juffrouw replied that *Jongens Sato* wasn't his name. It simply meant "Boy One."

Then she beckoned forward another of the men. Unlike elderly Boy One, he was a lad of twenty, so his title of Boy Two suited him well enough. Besides being young, he was handsome with his long-lashed black eyes and white teeth which he showed in a cheerful but slightly fatuous grin.

Mother wanted to know what Boy Two was and what he did. Juffrouw plunged into her English-Dutch dictionary which accompanied her as closely as her godown key. After much page turning and eye screwing, she took her head from her book to say that Boy Two was a flunkey.

Mother had heard of flunkeys but she had never seen one in action, so she was in the dark about Boy Two's activities. And in the dark she was to remain because Boy Two never did anything but stand around in the dining room while meals were being served. In fact, he didn't even stand but leaned gracefully against the sideboard wearing his cheerful but fatuous grin.

Boy Three, who followed Boy Two, was less striking. We later found out that he was responsible for polishing the tile floors until they were as slippery as ice.

Besides the three houseboys, we also had a chauffeur. Mother said we didn't need one as both she and Dad drove. But Juffrouw replied that we needed a chauffeur because none of the Dutch in Java did any physical work and driving a car was hard work, wasn't it? Besides, the man was paid only thirteen dollars a month and the other servants were paid even less. Mother, who found it difficult to disagree with Juffrouw, said that at that wage we could perhaps afford a chauffeur.

The man didn't seem to have a name or a number but was called simply Chauffeur. Apparently he agreed that driving was hard work because he had an assistant, a small boy called Amat. Amat would make himself useful, Juffrouw said, by riding beside Chauffeur and opening the car door for us. Even at his wage of five dollars a month, Amat didn't seem very useful to Mother. She decided he should be dismissed. But by the time she got around to it, Amat and our boys were such friends that Amat stayed on as a playmate.

The gardener was not as fully dressed as the other men, being naked above his tucked-up, outdoor-model sarong. He had a helper too, a lad of fifteen who was even more airily attired in only underpants and a hibiscus behind one ear.

After the last and least of the men servants had left

the room, the first of the women stepped forward. She was Boy One's wife and matched him in age and dignity. Mother asked her name and Juffrouw explained that one didn't call the natives by their own names. In Malay, a woman is a *Baboo* and Boy One's wife was *Baboo*, or Woman Cook.

At this point Juffrouw decided to give us a short lesson in Malay. Married women, she said, are called *Nonya Besar*, or Mrs. Big. Unmarried women are *Nonee*, or Miss. Gentlemen are called *Tuan*, or Lord; and the head of a family, like Dad, is called *Tuan Besar*, or Lord Big. So Dad and Mother were, to the servants, Lord Big and Mrs. Big.

Orang is the Malay word for "man" and also for "men" because Malay is such a simple language that words have no plural form. One man is *orang* and several men are *orang-orang*. The Javanese call themselves *Orang Javas*; the Dutch are *Orang Blandas*, or "Man Blonds"; and we, the Strykers, were *Orang Americas!*

Juffrouw started to tell us the Malay titles of the rest of the servants. But Mother and I felt we had had enough Malay for one day so we asked her to please just tell us their names.

Aritita, the chambermaid, was young, pretty, and very dressy in her waist of fine lawn edged with lace and fastened with a gold brooch. Her heavy knot of satiny black hair was held with gold combs and into it was tucked a yellow champac flower.

Manisan was older, plump, untidy. As she stepped forward, she began to giggle like an idiot. Juffrouw explained that she was the nursemaid. Of course the boys didn't really need a nurse but Mother again found it easier to agree with Juffrouw than to argue.

Besides Manisan, Aritita, and Woman Cook, there was a Woman Wash and a Woman Sew. Last of all came the kitchen maid, an exceedingly ugly old woman named Sora.

After the women had been dismissed, Juffrouw jumped up, exclaiming that it would soon be lunch time. She must open the godown and give Woman Cook what was needed for the meal. Mother asked what we were having for lunch but Juffrouw replied that she would see when the time came. Mother started to ask when the time *would* come but Juffrouw had hurried off with the godown key in her hand.

Lunch, it turned out, was late because Dad didn't get home until one. He arrived, not in our own car, as we had expected, but in a taxi. He was red, damp with sweat, and in a bad temper.

He had spent the entire morning down at the custom-house but had not yet gotten our things through. He had merely filled out the forms and papers necessary to get them cleared. You'd think, he said, he was trying to bring in contraband arms or narcotic drugs instead of merely food, clothing, and an automobile.

The Dutch customs officials all knew some English and were very helpful and polite. But Lord, were they slow and had they given him a lot of papers to fill out! He'd have to go back after lunch and maybe stay there another hour or two.

17

Though lunch was so late, there was no food on the dining table, not even bread and butter. But there were some large soup plates which looked promising. Boy One appeared, however, not with soup but with rice. He made us understand that we should put it on our soup plates. Just plain rice wasn't very tempting and so we were glad when Boy Two came in with some chicken stew.

We liked chicken and rice and were about to plunge in when Juffrouw raised her hand forbiddingly. We weren't having just rice and chicken, she said, but the famous national Javanese dish of *rijst tafel*, or rice table. A great many other things besides chicken went into *rijst tafel* and we must wait for them.

After his initial effort with the chicken stew, Boy Two had taken his graceful pose against the sideboard but Boys One and Three were very busy passing us one dish after the other.

We obeyed Juffrouw's orders to take some of everything but couldn't help glancing at her incredulously. Curried lamb on top of chicken and rice? Then, hard-boiled eggs, sliced cucumber, bananas, peanuts, and chutney? But Juffrouw kept her eyes sternly fixed on us and we continued to heap our plates. Even when it came to strange things we had never seen before—tiny, inch-long fish in red sauce, crackers flavored with shrimp, and blue beans.

Then, still under Juffrouw's eye, we obediently stirred everything together. Hesitantly, very hesitantly, we took a taste. Not bad! Not bad at all, we decided as we tasted

18

some more. Good, very good indeed! as we really dug into it. Wonderful, marvelous! when our plates were empty and we were nearly bursting.

Dad rose from the table not quite so hurriedly as he had after breakfast and said he must be off. Juffrouw said he couldn't do that, not right after lunch. He must stay home and take a siesta. But Dad didn't have any time for napping. Politely but firmly he asked Juffrouw to phone for a taxi. When it came he jumped in and off he went, urging the driver to hurry up, please.

Juffrouw turned to the rest of us with a look that meant she would take no more nonsense. Lord Big, *Tuan Besar*, was too big for her to boss, but *we were going to take naps*. All of us, even Mother, had had enough of Juffrouw's bulldozing and *we were not going to take naps*. We were adamant in our decision for about fifteen minutes. Then our early rising, the oppressive heat, and our tremendous lunch defeated us.

Now we knew why an afternoon siesta was a custom of the country. After a midday *rijst tafel*, it was impossible to stand up. Juffrouw didn't have to say a word. We staggered to our rooms, untangled our mosquito nets, and passed out dead.

When we awoke an hour later, we bathed, changed, and felt a lot better. The boys were dying for something to do. There didn't seem to be anything to do except tease the parrot. But the poor bird, having been teased since early morning, was all worn out and merely sat on his perch and sulked. If only Dad would come home with the car, we could all take a ride and see the sights of Batavia.

But it was past six when Dad finally drove up in our car. As before, he was red, sweaty, and bad-tempered. When he had reached the customhouse after lunch it was empty because everyone was at home taking naps which lasted until midafternoon. The Javanese stevedores and dock hands were on the spot but they were lying around the piers and sheds sound asleep. When the customs officials finally got back on the job, our things had been cleared but our trunks and crates wouldn't be brought to the house until later.

And he had been told, Dad went on, redder and hotter than ever, that tomorrow he would have to go to the office of the Immigration Department. It seemed that the three hours we had spent with the immigration officials on our arrival was not sufficient. More red tape to go through, said Dad, and it would probably take most of the next morning.

Though one rose early in Java, everything else seemed to be very late; dinner was not until seven-thirty. Since we had had *rijst tafel* for lunch, Juffrouw said, we were having a light evening meal, just a roast with potatoes and macaroni. Mother, feeling that potatoes and macaroni were very starchy, suggested fruit for dessert. "But only the native eats fruit," said Juffrouw, as Big One marched in with a bread pudding which was followed by cheese and crackers.

After our light repast, Juffrouw didn't need to tell us at what time one went to bed in Java. Having had naps, we weren't exactly sleepy but just, as Jim put it, "kinda paralyzed."

Dad, the only man awake in Java that afternoon, was not only "kinda paralyzed" but sleepy as well. But he wasn't able to get to sleep. Besides having voluminous mosquito nets, our beds were furnished, not with pillows, but with tremendous, long, fat bolsters as hard as rocks. We children could sleep without pillows. Mother was inclined to put up with discomfort but Dad revolted against his rocky bolster. After a great deal of tossing and turning, he got up and knocked at Juffrouw's door.

When she had opened it and stood revealed in her cotton bathrobe and curl papers, she gave a gasp and recoiled. As though, Dad said later, he had ulterior motives. But all he wanted, he told her, was a regular pillow, the kind you could sleep on without breaking your neck.

But there were none, Juffrouw said, none in the house and none in all of Java. Pillows weren't used as they made one too hot and the bolsters weren't used for the head either. One flung an arm or leg over them for greater coolness.

The bolsters were called Dutch Wives. We thought that a funny name until we had been in Batavia a while and saw what *rijst tafel* had done to some of the Dutchwomen's figures.

21

NEXT morning Dad got up at five. Since the rest of us were up and running around, he thought he might as well conform with that custom. But not, he was determined, with customary Javanese slowness in general. He would be at the Immigration Office when its doors opened, fill out those papers, and get out again in a jiffy.

Immediately—that very day, if possible—he must start to see about buying his tapioca plantation. Most of the plantations in Java were owned by the government so Dad would have to deal with the officials of the government Land Department. His lengthy sessions with the customs men made him suspect that all Dutch officials might be a little on the slow side. As Dad wanted to buy his plantation within a month, he had no time lose.

Mother also rose with the intention, in her milder way, of running counter to the customs of the country. Getting up at five was all right since it was so hot later in the day, and a nap in the afternoon was all right too. But Mother was determined to do something about those tremendous meals Juffrouw served us, twice as much as we could eat and so heavy and starchy.

Mother knew that it would be difficult to make Juffrouw accept any suggestions, but after breakfast she screwed up her courage and told Juffrouw we would like a light lunch that day, just cold consommé and a salad. Also, Mother went on, she was going downtown that very morning and get some fresh vegetables and fruit, even if only the natives *did* eat them.

Dad got up from the table hurriedly and said he was off to the Immigration Office. Juffrouw also rose hurriedly as though falling in with Dad's plans. Only, she said, there wasn't any use going downtown yet. Nothing in Batavia, neither stores nor government offices, opened until nine-thirty or even later.

"Then what's the point of getting up at the crack of dawn?" said Dad angrily and strode off into the house.

Mother said that since it would be several hours before she could do any marketing, she would go out and look over the kitchen and Juffrouw went with her.

Just as our bathroom didn't look in the least like a bathroom, our kitchen didn't look at all like a kitchen. It had no stove or sink and the icebox was kept in the godown along with everything edible except the salt, which the natives, apparently, could be trusted not to steal.

Although breakfast was over, Woman Cook was crouched on the floor beside a small charcoal brazier on which stood a pan of boiling water. On top of the pan was a basket of rice which after three hours' steaming would be ready for lunch, Juffrouw said. Mother reminded her that we didn't want rice for lunch, just a salad and consommé. But the servants wanted rice for their lunch, Juffrouw replied. Then she stooped over one of the many other braziers surrounding Woman Cook and solicitously stirred a concoction of the tiny, red fish we had had with our *rijst tafel*.

When they left the kitchen, Juffrouw unlocked the godown door and let Mother have a peep inside. It was large, dimly lit, and seemed to be piled to the ceiling with bags of rice. Whatever we might like, our servants, like all the Javanese, lived on it almost entirely. Mother was glad when nine o'clock came round and she could start off to get some other food.

Chauffeur brought the car up to the door and not only was little Amat squeezed in beside him, but Boy Three as well. Dad didn't think we needed a chauffeur and, of course, little Amat was entirely unnecessary. But what was Boy Three doing there? Juffrouw explained that he was coming along to carry our bundles and packages because it wasn't customary for the chauffeur to do that. Confronted with this new custom, Dad was inclined to argue but he was in a hurry, of course, so he got into the car with Mother and Juffrouw.

With three in the front seat and three in the back, there wasn't much room left. The boys began to fight about which of them should go. Dad said, just for that, they would all stay home. So I squeezed in the back seat and we drove off, leaving the boys still fighting.

The street, with its green lawns and tree-shaded walks was, as the boys had said, very much like home. The low, white, red-roofed houses might have been in California. When we reached the center of town, there were large modern stores, hotels, office and other buildings similar to those in any American city.

Dad had been right. There were lots of things in Java besides sand, palms, and natives. As to there being a lot of Javanese, he had been right about that too.

The sidewalks were thronged with little, brown people in their gaily printed skirts—some of the men wearing big, round straw hats on top of their turbans; some women under red, wax-paper parasols. Among them were a few pigtailed Chinese soberly clad in dark blue or black and some Arabs in long cloaks and bright red fezzes. There were comparatively few Hollanders on the streets and even in Batavia one realized that the Dutch were only a handful among Java's many millions.

We left Dad at the Immigration Office, standing impatiently before the door which was still closed.

We drove on to the square where the native market was held with its innumerable stalls and sheds full of chickens in coops, tubs of live fish, and mountains of fruit and vegetables. The place swarmed with people and was loud with the voices of vendors crying their wares or bargaining with their customers.

Our marketing took a long time because Juffrouw insisted on arguing over the price of each individual orange and lemon. She began by asking, *"Brapa?"* ("How much?").

When she was told the price she raised her eyebrows, threw up her hands, shrugged her shoulders, and turned away. Then the vendor would call after her, naming a lower price. At this she would mention a still lower sum.

25

This was the vendor's turn to raise brows, throw hands, and shrug shoulders. Juffrouw would refuse to raise her ante. Then the vendor would groan, wring his hands, and almost sob as he handed the purchases over to her.

"A Dutch housewife doesn't buy without bargaining," said Juffrouw triumphantly.

When we had finally completed our purchases, Juffrouw said they couldn't be carried home in the car. It wasn't proper to ride in a car piled with packages. Boy Three and little Amat would take our things home in hired carriages.

We didn't know why two carriages were necessary until we saw them; tiny, two-wheeled carts pulled by miniature horses. The weight of the driver on the front seat of a little cart tipped it down almost to the ground.

When Boy Three got into a cart with his packages and sat at the back, the driver flew up into the air. Boy Three drove off with his feet dangling in the street. Little Amat's driver weighed about the same as little Amat and his bundles so they drove off in a more or less horizontal position.

I wanted to ride home in one of the little carts too. Juffrouw protested that it was not proper for a young girl to ride around alone, but Mother said she was sure I would be quite safe and we need not worry about being proper.

My driver was a big, heavy man and his seat was practically down on the ground. My weight made no impression on the balance of the cart. I rode home leaning against the driver's back and with my knees up under my chin.

It was a slow trip and when I got there, Mother and Juffrouw had already been home for some time. Not long enough, however, for the consommé, lettuce, and

tomatoes Mother had bought to be used for lunch. Woman Cook hadn't had time to prepare them, Juffrouw said, so we had *rijst tafel* which happened to be all ready for us.

After lunch, Juffrouw told Dad she hoped he would take a siesta and not go out in the broiling sun again. Dad said he planned to spend the afternoon in his room. But not sleeping; he would be very busy.

At the Immigration Office Dad had been presented with a tremendous sheaf of forms and questionnaires to fill out. They were all in Dutch, of course, so the polite official kindly spent the morning explaining the questions to Dad who wrote copious marginal notes in English. By noon, he had not gotten around to actually answering any of the questions so the man suggested that he take them home with him. And no need to hurry back after lunch, the Dutchman said, as the office wouldn't open again until three-thirty. Dad could just take his time.

Dad shut himself in his room and took time—a lot of it. Reading the papers over, he realized that in spite of the kind official's help, some of the questions were not quite clear to him. Again he had to knock on Juffrouw's door and awaken her from her nap to translate some of the questions for him.

Then Dad took up his pen, squared his elbows and tackled question one, which asked the names and the date and place of birth of both of his parents. He went on from there, through his own birth, marriage, and the births of his children. Then he had to awaken Mother to ask where and when her parents had been born so that he could fill out a similar form for her. There were also forms for each of the children but, as we had not yet been married nor had offspring, that didn't take so very long.

Having fully identified himself and his family, Dad turned to the next paper which required a detailed statement of his financial status. Fortunately our trunks had arrived and been put in the storeroom. It took no more than three-quarters of an hour for Dad to find the right one, open it and get out his checking account, bank statements, and income tax receipts.

By five o'clock, Dad was well under way and was setting down his bank balance for the year 1920. When Juffrouw put her head in the door to ask if Dad would like some tea he said no. Perhaps by midnight, he thought, he would get around to counting the loose change in his pockets and then the job would be done.

At first the rest of us had refused Juffrouw's invitation also. But the tea table on the lawn was a pleasant place to sit, so Mother and I decided to sit with our housekeeper and have a cup or two ourselves. Soon the boys came and helped Juffrouw at her lonely task with the stacks of cake, buns, and cookies. But the boys couldn't help her with the sandwiches because they didn't like cucumbers.

Boy One, who was hovering about, was concerned about the boys skipping the sandwiches. He knew that those big crates which had arrived contained food. American food, Juffrouw had told him—exotic things these strange *Orang Americas* are fond of. Boy One hurried to open a crate so he could find something to tempt the boys' flagging appetites. Then he hurried back to the table and proudly set down a large platter—of tuna fish garnished with canned peaches and liberally sprinkled with corn flakes.

4

OUR helpful friend, Mijnheer Verstoffen, had spoken truly. Things *did* move slowly in Java. Slower, Dad said, than he had ever seen things move before. It had taken him, not an afternoon, but three whole days to fill out his entry forms for the Immigration Department. After the kind official had spent a day in carefully going over them, he said that Dad would soon receive the papers which would make him and his family bona fide residents of Java.

But until he got them, Dad was told, he could not take any steps toward purchasing land. He did not receive the papers until April, a month after our arrival, when he had expected already to have his plantation. It was only then that Dad could sit down and write to the Land Department regarding it. The department apparently didn't have a list of available plantations lying on its desk. So a reply came saying that the tapioca plantation situation would be looked into, considered, and Mijnheer Stryker would be informed about it in time. Dad tried to find out how much time but no one seemed to know.

Though Dad spent so much time filling out forms and writing letters, he also had to see a great many people in person. In this way he became acquainted with a number of Dutchmen, most of whom were government officials of one sort or other.

The East Indies government, besides owning much of the land in Java, also owned the public utilities and ran the railroads and almost everything else on the island. This required a tremendous administrative machine and a considerable portion of the Dutch were employed in it. The vast administrative hierarchy was headed by Mijnheer the Governor General of the entire East Indies. Under him was the Governor of West Java and then the Resident, or head, of the Batavia district.

The two governors were beyond the ken of most mortals but our parents were invited to call on Mijnheer the Resident. Still that dignitary didn't return the calls of persons who were below a certain rank in the hierarchy. Whether we Strykers were socially beneath the Resident or whether it was just that we were not a part of the administrative system, Mother and Dad could not decide. At any rate, Mijnheer the Resident didn't call on *us*.

The other, less lofty personages who did went about it very ceremoniously. After Dad had met a Mijnheer in the course of his negotiations, Mijnheer would send

Mevrouw, his wife, to leave cards at our house. But Mevrouw wasn't supposed to see Mother during the card-leaving because they had not yet been formally introduced.

At first Mother didn't know that. She thought that Mevrouw had come to call and would make her sit down and visit. But Mevrouw would be obviously ill at ease. She didn't like to visit a person to whom she had not been introduced by a third party. It wasn't proper and it wasn't customary. When Mother came to realize that, she learned to hide during the card-leaving.

After the cards, came the first call which was arranged well ahead of time and with all of the formality we would use in planning a formal dinner party at home. But in Batavia one didn't begin to dine together so soon. The first visit was only for tea.

Apart from Verstoffen, who dropped in from time to time to remind Dad about slowness, our first formal callers were the De Witts. Mother and Dad, of course, returned their call but without any preliminaries. They just dropped in on them.

That was wrong, completely wrong. Afterwards, they knew they should have realized it as soon as they reached the De Witts' house because the De Witts weren't on their front porch. They were not, as the French say, "visible." Meaning, not that they had vanished into thin air, but merely that they were not prepared to receive callers.

The Dutch, when not visible, sat on their back porch and that's where the De Witts were at the time. But

Mother and Dad, ignorant of that custom, went barging right out.

Mevrouw De Witt was caught in her invisible costume—a sarong and shirtwaist—but she bore up bravely and offered her visitors tea. Mijnheer De Witt pulled himself up from his chaise longue and scratched his head. He just didn't know *what* to do. Like Mevrouw, he wore a sarong—but nothing else. His big belly sagged ponderously over his flowered skirt and he wriggled his bare toes in embarrassment.

After that, our parents didn't drop in on people. They began by leaving cards, then gave due warning of their visits as was customary and proper.

Our callers, of course, were in their *visible* costumes. The men all wore starched white linen suits which, for some reason or other, had high, stiff collars like military uniforms. Those tight collars were probably one reason that they were so prone to strip and collapse on their chaise longues on their back porchs.

Though the men wore what was practically a uniform, the women's clothes were in an infinite variety of styles because they renewed their wardrobes on their periodic leaves at home in Holland. Vacations at home occurred fairly frequently among the higher-ups so the more important ladies were dressed more or less in the current modes. Others, the wives of mere postal clerks, for instance, got home only once in seven years and their clothes were correspondingly out of date. Of course, their dresses didn't last that long so the original models were copied over and over again by the Women Sews.

33

One could tell at a glance which was Mevrouw the wife of the head of a department by her new clothes and which the wife of an underling by her long-outmoded dresses. But whether in or out of style, the Dutch women were not remarkable for their chic. They wore their dresses loosely over their generally plump and corsetless figures. Though corsets were not considered necessary, petticoats were *de rigueur* and were worn drooping well below the hemline. When Dad told Mother she was probably the only woman in Java whose slip didn't show, she positively blushed. It was a real compliment!

Besides their teatime calls and formal dinners, the Dutch had their club which our parents joined, hoping it would prove a little jollier than the very slow social whirl. But at the club, apparently, all one did was sit. The men did their sitting on the terrace where they consumed quantities of beer or gin and bitters while they watched people passing by. Dad didn't spend much time on the club terrace. For one thing, he didn't care much for gin and bitters or *pijts*. For another, he said the ankles that passed by weren't worth watching for very long.

A break in terrace sitting came on Queen Wilhelmina's birthday when not only Holland but all the East Indies rejoiced and a dinner dance was given at the club.

The dinner, which began with a great many cocktails, was constantly interrupted as first one and then another of the guests rose to toast their Queen. The Dutch were too polite to ignore the presence of two Americans so a number of toasts were proposed to the President of the United States as well. This meant that each time

34

Dad had to rise and toast Queen Wilhelmina in return.

When the dancing finally began, all the couples had to assort themselves according to their position in the hierarchy. Mevrouw Resident opened the ball with Mijnheer Assistant Resident, whose wife danced with Mijnheer Resident himself. Mevrouw Chief Controller danced with Mijnheer Assistant Controller and so it went all the way down to the sewage department represented by timid, little men and their wives in their seven-year-out-of-style dresses.

While the hierarchy were doing their duty dancing, Mother and Dad were left out in the cold and had to dance with each other which, as a matter of fact, they didn't mind at all. The Dutch continued their merry round until Mijnheer Resident had danced with one of the dowdy sewage ladies and his wife had had a whirl with one of the timid sewage men. Then everyone could choose the partner he wished and the real fun began.

Not only the dinner but the dances had been interrupted by toasts to the Queen. By midnight, many of the Dutchmen were drunk, and very drunk. Inhibited by their high collars, formal manners, and protocol, when the Dutch let themselves go—*they let go*.

Finally the club ballroom wouldn't hold them. They danced out onto the terrace, down the steps, and into the streets where they joined other happy throngs from the restaurants and hotels where, of course, celebrations were also being held.

Big, pink Mijnheer Verstoffen appeared from somewhere and seized upon Mother. He clasped her tight

35

and whirled her along the street like an ardent but un-
steady elephant. When he finally, after a long time,
whirled her back into the club, Mother had to go to the
ladies' room to lie down and recover.

Mother insisted that Dad could have rescued her
from the elephantine Verstoffen if he had wanted to.
But Dad had been waltzing through the streets in the
arms of a Rubensesque blond. At every glance of distress
from his wife, he had merely laughed and cavorted off,
hugging his blond the closer.

Afterward he explained that all those toasts to Queen
Wilhelmina had perhaps slightly affected him. Also, the
blond had been hugging him so tightly that he couldn't
get away from her.

"That's all very well," Mother said. "I don't object to
your getting high or dancing with plump blonds. But if
that man Verstoffen had stepped on me I'd have been
mashed to a pulp!"

5

WHILE our parents were conforming or, one might
say, slowing down to the usual pace of Dutch social life,
at home we also fell into the customs of the country.
And we found them pleasant enough once we got used
to them.

Even if we had not found them so, we would have conformed anyway, because we were helpless under Juffrouw's small but iron thumb. Like a general commanding an army, she got us up at dawn, saw that we bathed twice a day, and put us to bed for our naps. In regard to our meals, Mother waged a gallant but losing fight. Though she was able to insist on some fruit and vegetables, Juffrouw retaliated by insisting on afternoon tea. So on the whole we were still eating our heads off, just as before.

We became if not exactly at home, at least used to our tremendous rooms and slippery floors and even somewhat reconciled to the blue living-room set and potted palms.

We also became familiar with the strange creatures that lived in the house with us. Besides bugs and insects of every sort we had ever seen, there were big, black beetles that ate the toothpaste right through the tube and chewed the bindings off the books. There were also tarantulas as big as saucers and looking like a cross between a spider and a crab.

Other odd creatures were the geckos, big lizards that came out from somewhere or other and walked around the walls and ceilings at nightfall. Some were over a foot long and they had an unpleasant habit of staring us in the eye and croaking—"*gecko-gecko-gecko.*"

We were told one mustn't try to get rid of them because they were good creatures that ate the insects. So we learned to stare coldly back at them when they croaked at us.

37

Some of the insects were also good—to eat. They were wasplike things that flew around the house as soon as the lights were lit. Manisan was particularly fond of them. Giggling madly, she would run around catching them and popping them into her mouth.

Out of doors everything grew and bloomed so exuberantly that we could almost hear them doing it. The sun rose from morning mists to blaze at white heat all through the day. Then it sank suddenly and fiery red and, in a moment, it was night. The night sky was deep, almost purple blue. The stars were bigger and brighter than those at home and so close it seemed one could reach up and touch them.

When we sat on the porch in the evening a light breeze came not from the seacoast and brightly lighted city but from inland. From the dark plain and the mountains which we saw as distant, blue outlines by day and towering, dark and mysterious, at night. The evening breeze came from the heart of Java somewhere away off there in the darkness.

We could hear too the notes of flutes drifting across the plain. Sometimes wooden gongs, or *gung-gungs*, echoed from village to village. Then, Juffrouw said, the natives were making *ramee-ramee*, or merry-merry. They didn't make merry very often but every night we heard the flutes calling and answering each other in the darkness.

Later, we began to know our servants who had at first been merely strange, little brown people. When Dad became convinced that Boy Two would never do anything but lean against the sideboard, he fired him—and fired him often. But Boy Two said he liked us. So no matter how often he was fired there he was back again at his old stand, lounging gracefully and giving us his cheery, idiotic grin.

Though Manisan giggled continually, she also managed to talk most of the time. She talked so much, in fact, that we began to learn some Malay from her. As commonly spoken it is such a simple language that besides having no plural form, it also has no past or future tense. In Malay everything seems to happen in the present, which is rather confusing, though it makes it an easy tongue to learn. We children picked it up quickly but our parents were slower at it. They couldn't get used to saying: "I go downtown," when they really meant that they had gone downtown a week ago.

Aritita, the maid, didn't teach us anything or even pay much attention to us, being merely distantly polite. But she became lively enough when Chauffeur was around. Like Boy Two, he was handsome and with his very high salary, he was a ladies' man and a dandy. When we went out to the *bad*, we would see him flirting with Aritita, who sat on the kampong porch chewing betel.

The otherwise attractively mannered Javanese have this repulsive habit which throws tobacco chewing quite in the shade because betel chewing makes the mouth look as though it is full of blood. It is quite alarming to see someone shoot out a stream of red spittle. Besides being repulsive while being chewed, betel turns the teeth black, but the Javanese admire black teeth and also prefer them short. At the age when an American girl gets her first permanent wave, the Javanese belle has her teeth filed so they won't be so long and ugly.

After learning that Aritita flirted with Chauffeur, we discovered that the old kitchen maid, Sora, was handsome Boy Two's wife. When she wasn't washing vegetables or dishes, she was devotedly rolling his cigarettes. Or he would lie with his head on her lap while she picked the lice from his hair and crushed them between her fingernails.

In addition to all the people who lived out in our kampong, perambulating street vendors frequently appeared balancing their wares at the ends of long, bamboo poles which they carried across their shoulders.

Some were complete, one-man restaurants. A charcoal brazier with live coals hung from one end of the pole and a large jar of pink lemonade from the other. They were prepared to serve complete *rijst tafels* on hot plates. They also carried cakes and cookies glistening with red, green, or yellow icing and venomous-looking candy. We children were not supposed to sample their wares but naturally we not only sampled but ate lots of them.

Besides the restaurant men, there were also Arab vendors called, for some reason or other, "Bombay Men." They peddled hand-wrought Javanese brass and silver bowls and trays and wood carvings. In addition to everyday sarongs of cotton batik, there were exquisite ones of handmade silk embroidered with gold or silver threads.

The Bombay Man generally arrived when Mother and Juffrouw were having coffee out on the back porch. After insisting on afternoon tea, Juffrouw had also introduced the custom of midmorning coffee—*en klein kof-fieje*—meaning just a "little, weeny coffee." And Mother had not only followed this custom, but, like Juffrouw, she had taken to wearing a sarong, shirtwaist, and mules around the house in the mornings.

The Bombay Man would set out his wares and Mother, who loved to buy things, would want to purchase them all immediately. But Juffrouw would restrain her with the remark that a Dutch housewife didn't buy without bargaining. Then Juffrouw would start with: "How much?" and go on from there with her brow-raising and shoulder-shrugging until she named a lower price. When he heard it the Bombay Man would recoil as though stung by an asp. But most often, in the end, he would accept the offer.

Occasionally, however, the Arab would keep shrugging his shoulders, then wrap up his wares and depart muttering under his breath that at the prices Juffrouw offered him his children would starve. Mother didn't want the man's children to starve and she also wanted to buy the beautiful things he sold. But Juffrouw wouldn't let her call him back. She said he would return of his own accord, which he generally did and accepted Juffrouw's offers.

Mother was somewhat inclined to indolence so it was well enough for her to while away her time over coffee and bric-a-brac. But we children didn't know what in the world to do with ourselves. When we asked Juffrouw what the Dutch children did with *themselves*, she was not very helpful. She said that they stayed in school until four-thirty and then went home and did their lessons.

But when we insisted that they must have at least a little recreation, Juffrouw recalled that there was a public swimming pool in town. So we spent a great deal of time there. On weekdays we had it almost to ourselves until late afternoon when the overworked Dutch kids arrived.

As they didn't know Dutch, my brothers used the little Malay at their command to become acquainted and pick fights. Picking fights was pretty safe, they thought, because the Dutch boys looked like such sissies. Even the great big ones wore short pants and round-collared blouses like tropical versions of little Lord Fauntleroy. But when it came to a showdown, our boys found that despite their short pants and round collars, the Dutch lads were a match for them, and in some cases, a lot more than a match.

Though the Dutch children were allowed to go swimming in the afternoon, none were to be seen after nightfall. They were presumably at home, studying their lessons. As we Strykers didn't have any studying to do, we frequently went to the movies.

It was in the days of silent pictures and instead of English captions, an explanation of the movie appeared written in Malay. Besides being simple, Malay is exceedingly terse, and the captions were brief and to the point. When the hero and heroine were spooning in the moonlight, the caption said: "Man wants woman." A battle between cowboys and Indians was explained by: *"Orang* Whites kill *Orang* Reds." When the heroine was unhappy she didn't have a sad heart but a sad liver. Because, to the Javanese, the liver is the seat of the emotions. They speak of people being big-livered, good-livered, sad-livered, or having a liver of gold.

The Javanese preferred Westerns and thought that all the *Orang Americas* were cowboys. They were very disappointed in us. The servants kept asking us if we were really *Orang Americas* or merely *Orang Inggris*, English.

Sedate, dignified Boy One was, unexpectedly, a movie fan. He was pleased to learn that Dad had done some riding and a little shooting as a young man. But *Tuan Besar* had not shot any Indians! Boy One could hardly believe his ears when Dad told him that he had never even *seen* any Indians. But we must know that wonderful *Orang Cow* named Tomma Mixo. How wonderful it must be in America with Tomma Mixo and the other *Orang* Cows and the *Orang* Reds!

"Oh, to be able to get away from it all," said Boy One. How he would like to be able to throw up everything, leave the humdrum of Java, and live the exciting, colorful life of the *Orang Americas!*

6

TIME passed, Dad continued to write letters to the Land Department and continued to receive no answers. Nothing seemed to be happening at all except that the weather, which had been hot and damp, was becoming hot and dry. We were told that the summer monsoon was commencing.

Java, lying just south of the equator, is always hot. The only changes in climate are due to the monsoons or trade winds which bring rain in winter and are dry in summer.

We didn't realize that we should do anything about the oncoming dry monsoon until the Rawleys took us in hand. They insisted that we should, we simply *must* leave the torrid heat of Batavia and spend the season somewhere up in the mountains. But of course Dad wouldn't do that. He wasn't going anywhere until he had bought his plantation even though the Rawleys told him that *everyone* in the Far East followed this custom.

The Rawleys were experts on the Far East and what one did there. Mother and Dad had met them at Queen Wilhelmina's birthday party and they had come to see us before leaving Batavia. After many years on their lonely tea plantation, they were anxious to be with English-speaking people, even though they were only Americans.

Now the Rawleys were English and as English as they could be. Since they had spent most of their lives in the East, they were perhaps more English than they would have been at home. They took the white man's burden very seriously.

Besides telling us that we *must* leave Batavia for the summer, they also said that our parents shouldn't have brought us to Java at all. They should have left us at

44

home in boarding school. If one brought one's children to the East, they became pale, puny, lethargic, unlettered, and ill-mannered. We could give them the lie in regard to paleness, puniness, and lethargy. But in manners we were perhaps not quite up to British standards.

Since we refused to move to the mountains, the Rawleys suggested that we come visit them at their plantation up on Mount Papandayan. But Dad said he wouldn't even take time for a visit because every day now he expected a reply from the Land Department.

It was May, two months after our arrival, when the reply finally came. After glancing at the letter, Dad didn't turn red but rather pale. The Land Department, the missive began unnecessarily, had taken time to consider Mijnheer Stryker's request to purchase a tapioca plantation. After due consideration, it had been decided that Mijnheer Stryker could *not* purchase a plantation! It was some time before Dad was able to continue the letter which explained the reason for this decision.

Finally he gritted his teeth and read on: Java was one of the most fertile and highly productive regions in the world. If the East Indies government allowed foreigners to buy land there, soon none of the island would be left to the Dutch. The big American and British rubber, sugar, and coffee companies would buy up everything. Of course, the Roselawn Glue Company wasn't a large concern. Nevertheless, it was a foreign company and the rule held in its case as well as any other.

"Rules!" snorted Dad. "Rules and regulations!"

When he read the letter's final paragraph he became a little less pale. Although the Land Department refused to sell Dad land, they were willing to rent him some on a very long lease and at a reasonable rental. After Dad had translated guilders into dollars, he decided that the rental *was* reasonable and that renting instead of buying might prove feasible. In view of all these disappointments and difficulties, some people might have given up their plan entirely. But not Dad. Dad never gave up.

So he set to work again to write and inquire about all the details in regard to renting land. He had learned, to his cost, that things went slowly in Java and knew it would be some time before he would get a reply.

Just then a letter came from the Rawleys renewing their invitation for us to visit them. Dad decided that we would go, not all of us, as the Rawley's had suggested, but only he and Mother, and Jim and I.

Peter, Frank, and Henry opposed his decision and quoted Mrs. Rawley's remarks about the effects of a hot climate on small children. But Dad wouldn't change his mind so they had to stay at home. Mother told Juffrouw that they mustn't live entirely on starches during the week we would be gone. Juffrouw promised to give them fruit and vegetables but sparingly, she said, so as to do them no harm.

It was very early when we drove off behind Chauffeur and little Amat who had decided he would like a trip to the mountains also. Few people were astir in Batavia but on the outskirts we met Javanese bringing their farm produce in to market.

High, wooden carts, elaborately carved and gaily painted, lumbered along, their drivers lying on top and finishing their night's sleep. The big, gray buffaloes drawing the carts could be trusted to find their way to the market. Many Javanese carried their wares, the men employing long shoulder poles and the women baskets on their heads. Since the sun had just risen, it was still somewhat chilly, so the men had their sarongs pulled up around their shoulders and the women were muffled in long scarves. But the little children trudged along stark naked.

After several hours, the mountains, which had been dim and distant, were near enough to show the pale green of crops on their lower slopes and the darker green of forests above.

When we reached higher ground, rice was growing on terraces cut into the hillsides. Farther, as the hills steepened, the rice terraces mounted their flanks like the steps of a giant's staircase.

To feed its millions, Java, except for its jungle, is cultivated almost to the mountaintops. And rice, the staff of life to the Javanese, is grown on every available foot of ground. The rice is planted in shallow water which is retained within the terraces by low balks of earth. During the planting season the terraces are pools which mirror every nuance of the sky and passing clouds. Then the young rice appears as pale, sparse stalks which thicken and deepen to a rich, waving green.

Now the crops were golden ripe and in the fields were strings to which were fastened varicolored strips of cloth like kite tails, which fluttered to scare the birds. The fluttering was done by a man who spent the day in a little, high-perched hut. There he lay comfortably on his back with a string tied to his big toe. When the birds swooped down, he idly twitched his toe, which set all of the other strings in motion and the birds flew away in alarm.

By the time we stopped for a picnic lunch we were high in the mountains. It was cool there because since early morning we had climbed from the tropic to the temperate zone. We could look down the terraced mountain slopes to the plain, glimmering green and gold under the midday sun.

By afternoon we had descended to a valley steaming with tropic heat and blooming with brilliant flowers. Then we started the steep ascent of Mount Papandayan which rose majestically into twin peaks.

When Chauffeur said that Papandayan was a volcano, Mother said the Rawleys must be crazy to live there and that we must be crazy to visit them.

Sensing her concern, Chauffeur tried to reassure her. As well as we could make out with our smattering of Malay, he said that most volcanoes were either dead or sound asleep. Papandayan had been sound asleep but had begun to stir of late. But it wouldn't be wide awake for some time yet, so we needn't be frightened.

Jim said he wasn't frightened at all and I rather feebly echoed him. Mother said nothing but kept her fingers crossed, while Dad explained that the Rawleys had been living on the volcano's flank for twenty years and there

was no reason to think it would erupt during the short time we would stay with them.

It was dusk and we were fairly high on Papandayan when we reached the Rawleys. We were glad to see the lights of their house which was a low, rambling place, set among big trees.

The Rawleys were at the door to greet us. They wore tweeds and a fire blazed in the open hearth in the hall. They gave our parents whiskey and sodas and Jim and I had tea. Sitting before the fire, we might have been at home in Pennsylvania on a crisp fall evening.

7

WE awoke to a bright, crisp morning and put on our sweaters. There was a fire in the breakfast room, and there we met the Middletons who were also visiting the Rawleys.

Dr. Middleton was a geologist who had been in the Far East for many years and he was now a spare, bent man of seventy. Due to his advanced age and to his interest in the remote past, he had come to be known as Father Time. His wife, equally aged and enormously fat, was known as Mother Earth.

We had tea for breakfast though we would have preferred coffee. Their tea, Mrs. Rawley said, was the finest mountain pekoe and we *must* drink it. Tea was the drink for the tropics. She never drank anything else, not even water!

Mrs. Middleton said that if the water were boiled it could be drunk just so. Adding tea leaves didn't kill the germs but the boiling did. Mrs. Rawley said she was wrong about that, *quite* wrong. Mrs. Rawley had been in the East for years and never drank plain, boiled water. One *must* add tea leaves to kill the germs. Mr. Rawley backed her up on that. He went on to say that adding whiskey to the water was just as efficacious as tea. He drank tea for breakfast but after that he subsisted on highballs and had done so for the past thirty years.

We spent the morning looking at tea, in its natural state on the bush, then cut, dried, and packed in crates. And at the end of three hours we were pretty tired of it.

At last we started back to the house, and lunch seemed to be in sight. But first, we *must* see the garage. A garage is a novelty in Java, but we didn't want to see it now. However Mr. Rawley's was a special kind of garage. There were two cars in it, each piled to the top with bundles, packages, and luggage. They were ready and waiting with everything the Rawleys would need for their getaway when and if Papandayan decided to erupt.

They had been caught in one eruption, Mr. Rawley said, when Mount Kloet blew up. They had had to run away in their night clothes holding a table over their heads to protect them from the volcanic ashes that fell like rain. Never again, said Mr. Rawley. This time they

51

were prepared. Everything was ready in the cars; tea, whiskey, toothbrushes, and all.

We remembered that Chauffeur had said Papandayan was beginning to awaken. But now Mr. Rawley laughed at our fears. Papandayan wouldn't erupt for several months and when it did, the lava flow would probably not descend as far as the plantation. The only inconvenience would be the fall of ashes. Mr. Rawley said that since the Kloet eruption he and his wife just didn't care for hot ashes. Silly of them, wasn't it?

There was always ample warning of an eruption, our host explained. Long before there was a sound or a movement from the crater, the animals knew by some sixth sense denied to men. First the wild animals knew and came down from the mountaintop. Then the domestic animals sensed it too. The cows walked out of their stalls and the horses from their stables. Even the house cats went off some night. But the dogs didn't leave. They knew too but they left—or stayed—with their masters.

The only living creatures who did not want to go were the people. Time and time again the Javanese had stayed in their villages with their little houses and rice fields until the lava came flowing in a dark, molten mass and it was too late.

Less reliable than the animals, Mr. Rawley said, were the scientists. There were a number of them up on Papandayan right now watching and recording its stirring into life.

We simply must go up and see the craters—there were

two of them—before we left, Mr. Rawley insisted. Mother said, some other time, when Papandayan wasn't stirring but securely asleep. All the more reason to go now, said Mr. Rawley. Next thing we knew Papandayan would have erupted, then we would have to wait until it cooled off.

There was no resisting the enthusiastic Rawleys. They got us up at daybreak and put us in the car. It was cold then but we would be much colder later on, our hosts told us, and lent us their extra, volcano-visiting over-coats. We went in their car, as our chauffeur was afraid of the *gunung api-api*—the mountain fire-fire. It was not only dangerous but was the abode of evil spirits.

We soon reached the forests and drove through them on a road that became worse and worse until finally it came to an end with a teeth-breaking jolt. Mr. Rawley was prepared for that. We weren't to turn around and come back just because the road ended. No, he had sent word ahead the previous day and guides and ponies awaited us.

We each had a little pony and each pony was accompanied by two guides. Until we got under way we didn't know why *two* companions were necessary for each pony. We were still in the forest but the ground rose steeply and was covered with boulders and huge rocks that Papandayan had tossed out in ages past.

Ours were presumably mountain ponies but they were not of the proverbially sure-footed sort. They stumbled up the slopes, then sat and skidded down. The guide at the rear helped his pony stumble up by pushing. The

guide at the head acted as a brake when the pony tobag-
ganed downward.

But after considerable time, the ponies took us up
beyond the timber line. An icy wind met us there when
we got beyond the trees. We were in another world, one
we had never seen—a dead planet where there was not a
tree, a blade of grass, or any living creature. Here,
through the ages, Papandayan had spewed forth its lava
and here it had cooled into fantastic shapes looming one
above the other in dark, rusty red like dried blood.

The path upward became narrower and at last so
narrow that there was no room for our ponies to stumble
and skid. We left them with some of the guides and
continued on foot.

The path finally came to a more or less level area where
the boulders stood on lava beds resembling a frozen red
sea. The path became a rocky ledge and the ground on
each sides softened and looked like a marsh. But it was
not marsh, it was mud—hot, and farther on—boiling.
The earth on either side of the path quivered with heat
and we could feel it through our shoes although the air
was freezing cold.

We rounded a tremendous boulder and came onto a
narrow ledge where the ground was burning hot. Below
us was a sheer drop of several hundred feet to the boiling
lava that belched sulphurous fumes and smoke.

It was impressive, terrifying. But our feet were hot,
our bodies cold, the fumes made it hard to breathe or
see, and we were really scared.

Beyond the crater we looked into, was another. A

narrow wall of stone separated the two smoking chasms and on the wall we could see men through the smoke and fumes. The people who lived near the top of the mountain fire-fire were not afraid of it. The wall between the two craters formed a convenient short cut across the mountain which they took and carried their burdens across. Some of the men had shoulder poles and stepped briskly along with their baskets jouncing out at each side beyond the path and over the craters.

On the crater rim was a group of small houses which the guides said had been built for the scientists. No Javanese would live that near to a crater. The spirits of the fire mountain were powerful. Foolhardy were those who lived near their abode.

It took us much longer to get down through the boulders than to come up. When we finally reached our ponies, they slid slowly down to the place where we had left the car. It was late when we got back to the Rawleys'.

They had tea and whiskey and sodas ready. As we sat down by the fire, they asked how we had enjoyed our trip. We said feebly that it had at least been worthwhile. We had never seen active volcano craters before and we would never, never see them again.

Dr. Middleton, who was very learned, talked until late at night. It wasn't exactly his field, but he was interested in volcanology. He envied those fellows up there, watching and recording every belch, every boil and bubble of the craters.

That night I shivered in my bed to think of the men up in the dark and cold on the crater's lip. I was glad

55

that Dr. Middleton had said that a guard kept awake and watched all night.

But maybe the watcher slept. For within a month Papandayan did not erupt, it merely quivered. And then with a shrug of its mighty shoulder, the mountain fire-fire tossed the intruders into its fiery depth, with their little houses, records, instruments, and all.

8

THOUGH by now he knew things went slowly in Java, Dad could hardly bring himself to stay a full week at the Rawleys. Perhaps the Land Department would let him have an answer quicker than he expected. But we were back soon enough because it was a month before the department got around to sending a list of plantations which were for rent. After his months of work only with his pen, Dad was wild to get into action. He put the list in his pocket and set out to look over the various properties.

When Dad left we felt very forlorn, as though we really were on a desert island. He had looked very handsome, we thought, in his white ducks, white shoes, and new panama as he drove off behind our natty Chauffeur. Little Amat had wanted to go too, so he could open the car door. But after several months in the constant company of his sons, Dad said he thought he could get along for a while without a small boy.

It wasn't long before he had to get along also without the car and Chauffeur. His search for a plantation led him into remote regions where the roads were mere tracks and he had to make his way by buffalo cart or on horseback. When he returned several weeks later, his whites were soiled and crumpled, his shoes muddy, and his panama was curled down around his ears.

But he had found his land! Soil that was just right for tapioca—ten thousand acres of it on the south coast at a place called Daringo.

All that remained to be done was to ask the Land Department to lease him that particular tract. Then things progressed speedily. In less than a month Dad received a lengthy document stating that Mijnheer Stryker was granted a lease of the Daringo tract for a period of seventy-five years. He was to pay a yearly rental—in advance. He was to use the land to grow tapioca—and nothing else. That part was all right with Dad. He hadn't come to Java to grow cabbages.

The document went on to say just how much tapioca he was to grow and the number of workers who were to be employed. It stated how the workers were to be paid, housed, fed; supplied with medical care, education, amusements; their holidays; and all sorts of things. The document's final page specified the number, size, and capacity of the workers' latrines.

That was all right with Dad. He had no intention of underpaying or overworking his employees; he wanted them to have medical care, education, amusements, holidays, and latrines. *Just so he could start growing tapioca.*

There was another unwritten clause in his agreement with the government which had come verbally from the head of the Land Department himself. It made Dad laugh and made us laugh too.

The Dutch, it seemed, had the fantastic notion that the Japanese might some day invade Java! Wasn't it ridiculous? Why, Dad said, the Dutch must be crazy! To invade Java, the Japanese would have to establish themselves in China, then they would have to come south, past the impregnable British base of Singapore. Would the British let them do that? Would the United States let them get that near the Philippines? We weren't a lot of damn fools, were we?

But the Dutch took the notion seriously and had thought it all out. The Japanese, they believed, would not try to land on the north coast of Java with its big cities of Batavia, Samarang, and the strong naval base of Surabaya. They would make their attempt on the more defenseless south coast of the island. That was where the Daringo tract was, right on the seashore. And, Dad chuckled, the Dutch really thought the Japs might try to land there some day!

They even—this was the most absurd part—told Dad he must set up a flagpole on the shore. He must have an American flag, a large one, on hand and when the Japs arrived he must run it up. The Dutch figured that, though the Japanese might dare to make war on little Holland, they would think twice before encroaching on the property of a citizen of the powerful United States of America.

Dad was conscientious about keeping his part of an agreement even if he thought it absurd. A tall pole was set up on the Daringo shore. Dad had to send all the way to Manila for a big American flag.

Years later, in 1941, when the Japanese reached Daringo they came not from the sea, but overland from the fortified north coast which they had conquered in only a few days.

But back in 1927, Dad was delighted to get his land on a seventy-five-year lease of assured and peaceful occupancy. He was glad he had not been able to get a plantation already started and in working order. Daringo was a jungle and Dad would have to start from scratch.

Scratch was where Dad loved to start. Capable and efficient, he liked to do things himself from the very beginning, thoroughly and in the way they should be done. He had located the best tapioca soil in Java, he would build the biggest and best factory. And he would produce the finest tapioca the world had ever seen!

Also, it would be cheaper in the long run.

The run, of course, would be much longer than Dad had originally expected. Having to start a plantation from scratch would mean a lot of time spent in clearing and planting. Then the tapioca crop would take a year to mature. Getting the project started would take more time, a lot more time and money than Dad had expected.

But the boys were delighted that Dad had acquired a

59

jungle. That was what they had come to Java for, they said. They couldn't wait to get down to Daringo in the jungle with all those wild animals. I wasn't sure I would care about lots of wild animals. But Daringo sounded rather like the spot where I had pictured us living a simple life under waving palms.

So we all got out our suitcases and began to pack. Jim suggested that we wouldn't take suitcases, just knapsacks might be better, he said.

Dad told us not to worry about suitcases or knapsacks because we wouldn't be going to Daringo for a while yet. We would have to wait until a house had been built for us and there were a great many other things to do before that.

"But aren't there any houses there now?" Mother asked.

Dad said there was a small native village. But we wouldn't want to live in a one-room bamboo hut, would we? The boys said they certainly would. But although Mother had thought a hut would be picturesque, when it came to it she didn't really want to live in one. So like a sissy she said it would probably be better for us to remain in Batavia until a comfortable house was ready for us at Daringo.

Dad was wild with impatience during his weeks of waiting in Batavia. He had already hired a man named Klaut to go down to Daringo, look the place over, and decide what should be done. As soon as he had been fairly certain that the government would rent him the land, Dad sent word to Mijnheer Klaut to start work

60

immediately. Now, with his lease in his pocket, Dad was going right back to help him get things under way.

Though he didn't usually give much thought to his clothes Dad felt that whites were not exactly the thing for jungle wear, so he took time to buy himself a planter's outfit. Then he tried it on so we could see how he looked. That was his big mistake.

When the boys saw Dad in his military khaki shorts and shirt, his high boots and tremendous sun helmet, they set up a howl. They *had* to go to Daringo right away! They couldn't wait until a house was built. They didn't need a house! They would sleep in a hut, a tent, or better still, on the bare ground like explorers!

Dad said there was nothing that would interfere with his work so much as having four little explorers underfoot. Mother agreed that they would be nuisances and sighingly added that probably she and I would be nuisances also.

She was resigned to our remaining in Batavia—until a letter arrived from Mijnheer Klaut telling Dad what he had done since he had gotten word to go ahead. He had built an inn. For among its many other stipulations, Dad's lease required him to build an inn at Daringo for the accommodation of any travelers who might journey into that remote region. And Dad had every intention of building an inn—eventually.

But to build it first of all: Dad tore his hair. What had Klaut been thinking of? To build an inn when there was so much else to be done: The village at Daringo was linked to civilization by a single cart track and any traveler who chanced there would have nowhere else to go but through the jungle to the desolate, uninhabited seashore.

Dad was still mad when he read the rest of the letter in which Klaut pointed out that when new land was opened up in Java, the leaseholder was required to build an inn immediately.

"Rules and regulations," snorted Dad. "They're driving me crazy. It's ridiculous to build an inn in a place no one will go."

"Yes, absolutely ridiculous," Mother echoed. But she looked very thoughtful and added: "So there's a comfortable hotel down at Daringo—"

"A comfortable hotel!" Dad exclaimed. "What are you thinking of? It's not a hotel. It's an inn, or rather just a rough shack, knocked together in a few weeks."

"It's an inn," Mother gently insisted. "And you know you said that there won't be any travelers there. Well, I think it's just the place for us. So we'll *all* go to Daringo with you."

Perhaps Dad remembered how insistent Mother had been that the whole family was to come to Java with him. Perhaps—who knows—he was sorry he had not put his foot down then. But now, by golly, he was determined to put his foot down. Inn or no inn, we were *not* coming to Daringo with him. It would take us several weeks to get ready and he wouldn't, he simply couldn't take time to wait for us.

"You don't need to wait for us. Go on alone," Mother said. "I'll pack up and bring the children down later."

Drawing a deep breath, Dad said slowly and distinctly, "The place is a jungle. You know—a big forest full of tigers and panthers, rhinoceros, boa constrictors, and others things that eat people."

"Boa constrictors don't," Jim piped up. "They don't eat people, they just squeeze them to death."

Dad ignored him and drew another deep breath. "As I've said, it's a jungle—"

"Yes, yes," said Mother. "I've seen them in the movies."

Dad went on, "The place is fifty miles from Wazi, the nearest town. It's an all-day trip on horseback. You can't bring the children down alone. You can't travel there without a man carrying a gun."

The need for an armed escort seemed to make an impression on Mother. She admitted she wouldn't be able to fend off tigers and boa constrictors all by herself. Nonetheless, her expression remained thoughtful. Also, she began to pack like mad and we began to pack like mad too. We knew we could rely on whatever it was Mother had up her sleeve.

Only Juffrouw was taken into her confidence. Juffrouw agreed to take charge of turning the house back to its owner. She also would pay off the servants, do our heavy packing, and send our trunks and crates down to Daringo later on.

The day before Dad's departure, Mother took us downtown. She had herself and all of us outfitted as planters or explorers in khaki, boots, and helmets. We bought six canvas duffel bags, put our extra shirts and pants into them and took them home with us in the car.

When Dad saw us march up the steps, helmets on our heads and duffels over our shoulders, he stifled a groan. Knowing he couldn't resist Mother any further, he feebly said this was just fine. But, since we were all coming it would, on the whole, be better to wait for a day or so. He planned to drive as far as Wazi where Klaut would meet him with a horse for the rest of the journey. As there would be seven of us, he would send Klaut word to get more horses.

The boys began to howl again. They could walk from Wazi to Daringo! It was only fifty miles and they would just love it!

Dad, worn to a frazzle, said, "Oh, all *right*."

9

NEXT morning when the car drove up, Frank and Henry, who were somewhat confused about things, were disappointed. They thought we were going to leave Batavia on foot, like gypsies.

Everyone was somewhat confused because it was only five o'clock and we had swallowed our breakfasts whole. Juffrouw dashed about frantically and got us and our duffel bags into the car where we were squeezed like sardines. Chauffeur had to come along so he could bring the car back to Batavia where it would be sold.

We were sorry to say good-by to Juffrouw. Though she was so stern with us, we felt she had our good at heart. Juffrouw was sorry, too. She was losing her job, for one thing. For another, she trembled to think what we would do when we were out from under her iron thumb. Would we bathe twice daily or only once? Would we remember to take a nap every afternoon? Would we eat enough rice or subsist entirely on vegetables and fruit?

By now Mother's Malay was adequate for any domestic situation. But was she the type to make a real Dutch housewife? Juffrouw doubted that she was of stern enough stuff. Whatever she did, Juffrouw said, Mother must *not lose* the godown key. Because the natives steal.

We couldn't tell whether or not our servants were really sorry to see us go. Manisan said: *"Ado, ado, ado."* Boy One said it had been an interesting experience to work for people who were compatriots of Tomma Mixo and the other *Orang Cows*. The others said nothing but stood in silent array to watch us drive off. Juffrouw fluttered her handkerchief and shouted admonitions until we were out of hearing.

It was late afternoon when we drove into Wazi. At the ramshackle little hotel we met Mijnheer Klaut who had just arrived from Daringo. Stout, bald, and red, he was ponderously polite when Dad introduced us, but he was obviously dismayed. He told Dad that children were not generally taken into remote, primitive regions. Also, he said hopefully, he didn't know how we could

65

get enough horses for all of us. When the hotel manager told him he had horses for hire, Klaut said regretfully that there was no reason why we couldn't start off next morning.

Dad pointed out to Mother that Wazi was the place nearest to Daringo that could be called a town. It was not much of a town at that. Apart from the ramshackle hotel, a store, and a post office, it was only a large Javanese village. There was no railway and the roads beyond were only tracks and paths. Chauffeur, Dad added significantly, was returning to Batavia next day—in case Mother decided she didn't want to live in the jungle after all.

Perhaps that night, on the lumpy bed which she had to share with Henry and me, Mother thought about changing her mind. But I guess she was afraid to. Her four little explorers might have turned on her and rent her limb from limb.

We were an imposing calvacade as we rode off next morning with the impressive Mijnheer Klaut in the lead. After him came Mother and we children. Dad rode last so he would be able to pick up any casualties. He was followed by a Javanese who led three pack horses with our duffel bags.

Dad and Mother knew how to ride. Jim and I had ridden for the first time on our trip up Papandayan. The others, as Peter put it, had never been "aboard a horse" before. But all the boys wanted to gallop off like cowboys. Dad did not stop them when they shouted: "Yipee! Yipee!" and flapped their reins. He knew that nothing,

66

not even dynamite, would induce Javanese ponies to hasten their pace.

In the clear morning freshness we followed a narrow road winding through villages where people were just going out to work in the fields. By midmorning the freshness had burned to still, steady heat and we had passed beyond the villages and rice fields.

We rode on a narrower track into treeless, rolling meadows which extended before us as far as the eye could reach. This didn't look like Java and, Mijnheer Klaut explained, it was *not* like Java. This area and beyond, all the way down to the coast, was desolate and sparsely peopled. The volcano of Krakatoa, in one of the worst eruptions in history, had covered the region with lava. That had been about fifty years before. Now the rolling meadows were grown with grass and the area nearer the coast was covered with jungle.

We rode at foot pace in a shimmering flame of heat and burning dust followed us along the path. After an hour or so, no one thought about galloping. We slouched in our saddles, dropped our reins and held onto the pommels.

At noon we stopped to eat the lunch the hotel had put up for us—cold *rijst tafel* and warm, bottled lemonade. Frank and Henry wanted to lie down on the spot and take their naps, but they were heaved back onto their ponies.

Jim and I rode between them with orders to keep talking so they wouldn't fall asleep. I chatted dutifully for a while. Then, with the heat and dust, sleepiness and

67

aching bones, I couldn't talk any longer. I didn't care whether the boys fell off or not. I almost wished they would because that would entail a halt.

The sight of a herd of cows in the distance roused us a little. We had not seen cows for a long time so we shouted, "Look, cows!"

Mijnheer Klaut turned and hissed at us, "Quiet, please! Don't shout."

He called a halt, went to one of the pack horses and got two rifles. He gave one to Dad who changed his place and went to the rear. As we drew nearer the herd, Mijnheer Klaut loaded his rifle.

"You wouldn't shoot the poor things?" Mother asked.

Klaut hissed again, "Quiet. They're dangerous. They may charge."

We stared in surprise at the cows, quite near now and staring mildly at us. Mijnheer Klaut, his rifle cocked, watched them as we rode past. I looked back and saw Dad turn in his saddle to watch them as long as they were in sight.

Mijnheer Klaut explained that the cows were *benteng* or wild cattle. Originally domestic cows and bulls that had been abandoned, had run wild, and become the most ferocious beasts in Java, surpassing even tigers in strength and fierceness. In fact, they would charge a tiger and kill it. They also sometimes charged horsemen or people afoot and made short work of them.

Later, we saw another herd of cows, up to their knees in grass and watching us with mild, mournful, moo-cow eyes. But they tossed their long, curved horns in an unpleasantly thoughtful and calculating way. Then they whisked their tails, turned, and galloped off like race horses.

In late afternoon the meadows fell to flatness. The jungle, boundary of Daringo, rose before us like a wall. We followed a tunnel-like path into green shadows where heat and dampness closed down on us like a pall. The trees rose to great height and under them a second growth of smaller trees, giant ferns and interlacing vines shut out the sky.

Mijnheer Klaut called for a halt and a rest, now we were out of the burning sun. I had wanted more than anything else to be able to get off my pony and try to pull my legs together. But I didn't like the idea of dismounting in the jungle. Dad persuaded me by saying that though there *were* wild animals about, there wasn't one behind each tree waiting to take a bite out of anyone within reach. Our explorers, who had been going to kill wild animals with their bare hands, needed a little persuasion also. As for Mother, she slid cautiously to the ground and stood holding her pony tight around the neck. Frank and Henry were too stiff to slide and had to be lifted down.

As nothing jumped out at us, we ventured to walk along the path and stretch our legs. We made trips behind the bushes, finished our warm lemonade, and were ready to start again. Dad took Frank on his horse, Mijnheer Klaut took Henry, and the little boys were soon fast alseep.

I was not only sleepy but ached from head to foot and

was dripping with sweat. I tried to take my mind off my troubles by admiring the jungle now that I was in it at last. Orchids flamed from the branches and the trees were burdened with blossoms entangled with lacy ferns and flowering vines.

But, I had to admit, I didn't like the jungle. It was silent and I didn't like its silence. I could hear, or rather, feel it as one feels rather than hears a person breathing down one's neck. It breathed like some tremendous creature asleep but ready to awaken. Hours passed while the green shadows deepened into purple and the narrow path became almost dark.

Then the jungle ended as suddenly as it had begun. We rode into an open space where the sky was still streaked with sunset. It was as damp and hot out in the open as it had been under the trees because we were on the coastal plain where there was not a breath of air even at nightfall.

Daringo village showed as a huddle of houses and faint lights in the clearing. As we rode through low-lying rice fields, some dogs barked, a few lights brightened, and a hollow drum began to beat. As we passed through the wooden palisade around the village we saw, by a flaring torch, the hollow drum that hung from a tree. Inside, the villagers stood at their doors to watch us ride by, but they were silent and motionless in the dusk.

The inn, dimly lighted, stood just beyond the village.

"Here we are," said Dad in a determinedly cheery tone of voice.

We were all too tired to reply. When Dad lifted Henry

from his pony, Henry uttered a feeble, "Hurrah! Here we are!" Then fell flat on his face because his legs were sound asleep. My legs were paralyzed too and when I slid to the ground, I gingerly tried them to see if they would go together again or if I was permanently bow-legged.

A blond woman came down from the porch holding up her lamp to peer at us in amazement. Mijnheer Klaut ceremoniously introduced his wife but she didn't ac-knowledge the introducton. She was staring at us in openmouthed astonishment.

"But *Himmel*—Heavens—there are only four beds! What were you thinking of, Albert, to bring seven people to sleep in four beds?"

"*Himmel!*" echoed Albert Klaut. What *had* he been thinking of? He should have insisted on our remaining at Wazi or returning to Batavia. Dad also wondered why it had not occurred to him that there might not be room for us all.

"The inn *is* rather small," said Mother mildly.

It was small—four rooms strung out along a porch. The walls were of woven bamboo matting and the roof was of thatch. Mother admitted that Dad had been quite right. It was not a comfortable hotel. Then she made her usual remark in a crisis, "Well, we'll just have to see what we can do."

"Yes, *Himmel!*" sighed Mevrouw Klaut. "We'll have to see what we can do."

Frank and Henry were carried up on the porch where they sagged against the wall like sacks of meal. The grownups sat around the rickety table and looked at each other. With Jim and Peter I sat on the steps and stared into the night.

I had never seen such darkness. The little village lights flickered like tremulous breaths. The purple-blue sky silhouetted the trees around the inn and beyond, the ragged blackness of the jungle. The silence palpitated like a heart and the voices around the table seemed to be the only sounds in the world.

They were talking, naturally, about beds. Mevrouw Klaut took the lead. She explained that as she and Albert lived at the inn, they would have to occupy one of the double beds. Mother and Dad would take the other and the three olders boys could occupy the third, while Henry and I would have to share the single one.

Then, becoming more cheerful, Mevrouw Klaut said, "Now, supper!"

From the kitchen, a small separate house, she brought the *rijst tafel* she had kept warm for her husband and for Dad. We divided it among us and each got a spoonful or two. Then we filled up our empty spaces with bread without butter and tea without milk.

Mevrouw Klaut lit the oil lamp in one of the bedrooms where Mother emptied our duffel bags onto the floor. When the three older boys had put on their pajamas, they squeezed themselves into bed. Henry was put to bed in another room.

I soon joined him, or rather, I attempted to join him on the narrow cot but it was difficult as Henry, already asleep, had his knees drawn up to his chin.

72

The lamp on the porch gleamed faintly through the air vent above the door. Voices droned for a little while then ceased and the light went out. Overhead, geckos scuttled in the thatch or scurried over the rough bamboo walls. Other, unidentifiable things, animals or insects, scuttled and scurried also. But outside was silence, the breathing silence of the night and of the jungle which seemed to have come closer.

I pushed Henry's knees out of my stomach. He rolled over and lay heavy and inert as children do when deeply asleep. Dear little fellow, I thought. I put my arms around him but he was as hot as a stove and sticky with sweat. Then his knees were up again and he stuck his fat bottom into my stomach. I pushed him away. Then he rolled over again and lay close to me with his knees under my chin. I climbed over him to the far side of the bed and lay against the wall. At least, he wouldn't be able to push me out of bed during the night.

10

I HEARD voices, faint and far, calling my name. But I didn't want to listen, I wanted to go on sleeping. Then the voices became louder, clearer, and more insistent. I would have to awaken. I sat up.

Bang! My head hit the bottom of the bed. Despite

73

my precautions, Henry had succeeded in pushing me out of it.

Mother had been first awake. After she saw I wasn't in bed, she had looked into the other rooms, then out in the bathhouse and even in the kitchen. When it seemed I was really not anywhere around, she rushed screaming to Dad.

Charlotte was gone! she shrieked. Charlotte had completely disappeared. A tiger must have come out of the jungle and eaten her up! And so completely, apparently, that not a scrap or morsel was left. Or had the tiger taken her off to devour at leisure in his lair? Oh, why had she been such a fool as to come to Daringo? Why had she brought her poor child to her death in the jungle?

Another thought struck her and she screamed again. Perhaps it was not a tiger but worse—some Javanese. Her daughter's maidenly charms were extremely meager —but had some dreadful man . . .

Dad, aroused from sound slumber, said he didn't think so. But he threw on some clothes and began to look around. The Klauts were also roused and began to search and call. The boys, terrified by Mother's fright, also began to shout. Mother, convinced that I was dead, just stood on the porch and screamed.

When I emerged from the bedroom, unsteadily and holding my head, Mother stopped in the middle of a shriek. She did not clasp me to her bosom but instead went into a rage. What did I mean by giving her such a scare? Where had I been? What had I been up to?

When I explained, she was angrier still. It was the

74

stupidest thing she had ever heard of! A great big girl like me getting pushed out of bed by a little, weeny fellow like Henry! And how, for heaven's sake, had I been able to sleep while everyone was shouting his head off?

Our breakfast of bread, cheese, and tea was prepared by a woman who came up from the village. Mijnheer Klaut and Dad ate hastily as they were in a hurry to be off. The boys ate hastily too because they thought that they were going off to start exploring at last.

When Dad said that they couldn't come with him there was a dreadful howl. What was the use of being all dressed up in boots and helmets if they couldn't explore? Dad replied that far from exploring, they were not to go beyond the immediate vicinity of the inn and the village.

But what, howled the boys, about all those tigers, panthers, and big snakes they had heard about? They were all right out in the jungle waiting for them, Dad said. And if any of the boys so much as put his foot in the jungle, he would whale the daylights out of him.

The boys sat scowling on the steps while Dad and Klaut walked to the village where they got their ponies and rode off to thrilling adventures.

Mevrouw Klaut helped Mother and me put things away. It was short work as we had so few things with us, also the only place to put them were on pegs in the bedroom walls or on shelves. Then Mevrouw suggested that we stroll down to the village and look around. The boys came with us, carefully maintaining their scowls, scuffling their feet, and complaining about the tameness of it all.

Jim was the most thoroughly disgruntled. He was in the jungle at last but all he could do was take a walk with his mother and sister! To show his disgust, he walked well ahead of us and at the side of the path, scuffling, growling, and throwing stones.

"*Hurrump. Hurrump.*"

Jim stopped in his tracks. Directly in front of him on a low branch sat a big, black ape *hurrumping*.

Mother could only let out a squeak. But Jim yelled in terror and we all ran. Mevrouw Klaut called us to come back, saying that the ape was entirely harmless. There were a great many apes and monkeys around and they never hurt anyone.

This particular ape was an orangutan, or man of the woods. Orangutans, the most manlike of all monkeys, have even the human characteristic of curiosity. This fellow had probably taken his place on the path for the express purpose of examining us. Reassured, we stood under his tree and examined him as he sat sedately with his hands on his knees staring at us.

"I think he wants to say something," said Henry who was not at all clear as to just what the creature was. It was a perfectly natural assumption. The orangutan's sad little eyes were as human as those of any man.

Perhaps, feeling embarrassed that he couldn't say anything, the orangutan gave another *hurrump*, rose, and climbed away in a deliberate manner.

Mevrouw Klaut said the apes and monkeys made their

home in the trees around the village and were so tame and friendly that they would come to live right in the houses if people would let them. The building of the inn, however, seemed to have frightened them away from that spot.

Later the monkeys ventured to return to the inn, brought back by their desire for the ripe, golden papayas that grew on a nearby tree. One afternoon we saw a big, brown monkey making his way across the fields, moving slowly and watching us intently all the while. As we made no movement, he cautiously climbed into the fruit tree. Still watching us, he carefully picked a papaya. Then, with a bound, he was out of the tree, across the fields and back in the jungle. There, his friends and relative who had been watching him began to chatter and cheer.

Others ventured to come for papayas. At first they ran off again immediately but later, since nothing alarming happened, they sat in the tree to eat. Still others followed and by sundown the tree was stripped bare.

But the monkeys remained and lived in the treetops where they watched us with keen interest all day long. At night we could hear them overhead stirring or chattering.

That first day we strolled through the village and saw nothing but a strange place. Daringo was only a clearing in the forbidden and forbidding jungle, a lost spot a million miles from nowhere. It seemed dull and uninteresting and we didn't like it.

When Dad returned at sundown after a busy day of

looking things over, we had nothing to tell him except about Jim's adventure with the orangutan. We said we didn't care for Daringo as much as we had expected. Because, we said, there was nothing there, just nothing at all.

11

THERE seemed to be nothing at Daringo because we were at last really in Java—a foreign land. Though in Batavia much had been new and strange to us, large towns are more or less the same everywhere. We had lived amid the trappings of our own familiar civilization. Daringo was so alien to us that it seemed, besides being far off and lost, empty and meaningless.

In time it would come to have meaning but at first we saw only externals. The village paths wound among the little bamboo and thatch houses. In the center of the village was the square, grass grown and shaded with tremendous waringin trees; and through it flowed the sluggish, little red-brown river.

Then we began to sense the charm of the place. It was as neat and well kept as a garden and, like a garden, embowered with trees and blazing with flowers; poinsettias, hibiscus, azaleas, flame vines, and mimosas which all seemed to be blooming at once. It was very quiet and at most times nearly empty because all of the able-bodied men and women were out at work in the fields. The children played quietly under the eyes of the old people who sat idly in the sun. One heard only the pound of a rice pestle, the bark of a dog, and the murmur of soft voices.

Along with their quietness, we noted the villagers' dignity. Though most had never seen *Orang Blandas*, or Men Blonds, before, no one, not even the children, stared at us as we walked about and gawked at them, their homes and their possessions.

Then, what had been only a stage-set with a few background figures, gradually began to come to life. In early morning and at evening the river was swarming with people who came to bathe, to wash their rice and vegetables, their children, and their big, docile buffaloes.

On the days when a market was held, mats were spread out on the village square and people came from around about to exchange their wares. They laughed, talked, and bargained shrewdly but without loudness or rudeness. Even the little children at play were quiet and gentle.

The chief personage of the village, the headsman, or mayor, lived in the biggest house on the square. Close by was the little wooden mosque where the Mohammedan priest presided and taught the boys to read and write.

A great deal of time was required to see more than the externals, which appeared in the ordinary round of daily life. The Javanese are not merely primitive brown people but part of an ancient and highly developed civilization, their tiny village and restricted lives are not meager and poor but a world in themselves, rich, varied, and meaningful.

All of this came slowly; probably not in its entirety during the time I was in Java but in thinking of it, learning more of it later. An adult knowledge of our own world is necessary to appreciate that of the Javanese. Their world is quiet and decorous, without hurry or noise, without ugliness or waste. It is characterized by an aesthetic sense which lends dignity to everything the people do and gives comeliness to everything they make and use.

The Javanese world is not only one of physical beauty but is rich in tradition and history. Java is the most important of the islands of the Malay Archipelago. Though the Portuguese were the first Europeans to discover them, the Dutch later appeared on the scene, after the Portuguese, and ruled the Indies until the Japanese invasion. Since then, after some years of turmoil, the peoples of the Indies have formed themselves into the Republic of Indonesia.

Though now Mohammedans, the Javanese were formerly Buddhists, converted by long-ago conquerors from India who made Java the center of a vast and powerful empire. The ancient Buddhist temples are in ruins, but the Javanese still remember and revere the old gods and heroes.

Even before Indians came upon the scene the Javanese had an animistic religion which endowed all nature and every creature with spirits which were adored or, more often, feared. These primtive beliefs are perhaps still the strongest. The sacred waringin trees on the village square have their daily offerings because no one dares to forget the ancient and fearsome spirits which linger in them.

Besides their religious beliefs, the Javanese live by a code of ancient customs handed down through generations and centuries. Their code, or adat, rules not only their behavior but their very thoughts and emotions.

At first adat meant to us only the Javanese way of doing things. But it is the way of the people, the climate, and the country. In time it was to have its effect on us and would, for good or evil, affect our lives and our fortunes.

That was far in the future. During our first days at Daringo we were merely spectators. Bored at the inn where there was nothing to do but eat and sleep, we were drawn to the village by the attraction of something, however quiet and placid, going on.

At first we merely stood around. Then our boys, the littlest ones first, began to play with the children. Jim and Peter, after watching the football games on the village square, began to join in. The boys had kites, wonderful big ones shaped like ships or dragons, and made their kites fight by smearing the strings with a mixture of glue and ground glass. The winner was he whose kite string cut those of his opponents. Cockfights were held on the square at night by torchlight. The boys and Dad became rabid fans.

But best of all was the river. Of course, Mother

wouldn't think of letting us swim in it along with the *Orang Javas*, the buffaloes, and everything else. But Frank and Henry began with what they called only wading. That was the opening wedge. After Mother found that they waded up to their waists, she let them put on their bathing suits. Then, of course, they waded up to their necks.

That, we said, was not wading but swimming. If the younger boys could swim so could we. Mother gave in and said all right. But we must swim upstream, so we wouldn't catch any diseases. She chose a spot for us and told us to stay in it. But little by little, drawn by the activities downstream, we drifted farther and farther down until we were swimming cheek by jowl with everyone else.

Mother tried to shoo us back upstream by saying that for all we knew some of those people might have leprosy. If any of them had leprosy, none of us caught it or anything else for that matter. We were even healthier in Java than we had been in Roselawn.

I was at the awkward age when I was too old to play. Besides, there was no one for me to play with as Javanese girls of my age were married women with families. I was also too young to sit on the porch with Mother and Mevrouw Klaut and talk or read.

So in the village, when I wasn't swimming, I stood and stared. I watched people at all the things they did out of doors and that was almost everything. They slept in their little houses but meals were generally served on their porches where a big, shallow basket of rice was set down. All of the family squatted around with their own cups which they filled from the basket. Each also had a small dish of condiments to put on his rice before he popped it into his mouth with his fingers. As in everything they did, they were quick and neat about eating.

And I soon learned that when the Javanese are doing something, they keep right at it. They don't dawdle or pause to scratch, stretch, or groan over a task as we do. On the other hand, when they are at leisure, their relaxation is complete. They squat on their hams, knees under chin, and silently stare at nothing. They are not lazy. The idea of the idleness of Orientals is false. Most of them live in such poverty, so close to destitution, that they all have to work hard. The notion that they are lazy comes from the foreigners who make the Orientals work for them. Are any of us industrious at work for which someone else reaps almost all the profit?

Besides being neat and tidy, the *Orang Javas* had daily baths in the river. These were conducted with decorum. The men bathed in one group, the women and small children in another. The women washed modestly, squatting in the water. Then they stood up, draped their sarongs around their hips and washed above them.

After their baths they put scented coconut oil on their hair, rolled it into a low knot, and generally put a flower in it. Then they stood naked for a moment and held their sarongs out lengthwise behind them. The ends were brought forward and folded in front in a

84

wide, flat pleat. In Batavia the women generally wore waists, but at Daringo they draped their sarongs high enough to cover their breasts. The men were generally naked to the waist and wore their sarongs tucked up like diapers or wore only short underpants. When they wanted to dress up they put on a cotton undershirt. But whatever their attire, they wore their turbans as *Tuan* Allah, the lord god, had ordained. Like the women, they often put a flower behind one ear.

Sarongs, turbans, and the women's scarves are always of batik—fabric printed in colors by the uniquely Javanese process of covering parts of the cloth with wax to resist the dye. The colors are not vivid and gaudy but show Javanese taste and restraint in their quiet rich tans, rusts, browns, and dull greens and blues.

Tiny children are naked except for a red string around their waists. When the strings are tight, their mothers know they have had enough rice. Their rice diet gives the toddlers big bellies and they strut around like so many little Santa Clauses. The heads of little boys are shaved except for a scalp lock. If they die before manhood, *Tuan* Allah uses the lock to snatch them up to paradise. Little girls don't need locks because females have no souls.

As we became used to our life at Daringo, it began to seem less empty, though our living was simplified to bare essentials. Having so few possessions, we were surprised to find how much of our time had been taken up with them. The trunks Juffrouw had planned to send remained in Batavia since they could not yet be trans-

85

ported. Our explorers' costumes reduced the clothing problem to almost nothing. Woman Cook took care of simplifying our diet which was exactly that of the *Orang Javas*.

But we were aliens and the lot of aliens in a strange land is idleness. The boys could play but Mother and I had little to do. So we did nothing, both being very much inclined to inertia under any circumstances.

12

WITH Dad, of course, the case was quite different. His life was not alien and idle. He was living the life of the country, the real life of any country—work. After his months of enforced inactivity, he went at it like a fire horse.

His first problem was transportation. As there was no railroad, everything would have to be brought to Daringo by water. Down on the coast was a fine bay which formed a natural ships' harbor. Since the coast was marshy the place for the factory, the workers' dwellings, and other buildings was the village which stood on higher ground and was supplied with water by the river.

There were four miles of jungle from the village to the shore. Klaut and Dad, with all the available local laborers, had immediately set to work to cut a road through. It was slow, hard work and both men were at it from early morning. Klaut and his helpers stopped in the afternoon for siestas. During that time Dad sat at his rickety little table and wrote letters, cast up his accounts and laid his plans.

Klaut stuck to his role of overseer. Dad was also an overseer but he was too energetic and too much in a hurry to stick to overseeing. He took an ax and hacked away as though he would be able to break through to the shore all by himself.

At the end of the day, talking things over, Klaut would tell Dad there was no need for him to fell trees himself. It took three men a month to clear an acre of jungle so the efforts of one man, however strenuous, would not greatly speed things up.

Then too, said Klaut, bringing out Juffrouw's favorite word, it was not proper for Dad to do physical work. He was the *Tuan Besar* and would lose face with the *Orang Javas*. It seemed that their adat applied not only to themselves but to everyone else too. It was not proper for a *tuan* to work like a coolie.

Dad said that he didn't care a hoot about Javanese customs. The road had to be opened as fast as possible, a dock had to be built at the shore, then a narrow gauge railway to haul things up to the village. Until then, nothing really important could be done. The tremendous job of land clearing would not get far without bulldozers.

"Bulldozers!" said Klaut, shaking his bald, red head. "No one in Java uses bulldozers. The *Orang Javas* don't

87

know anything about machines. I doubt if any of them could be taught to use them."

"I'll teach them all right, don't worry," said Dad.

Klaut was doubtful. He shook his head again and said, "Well, he who lives will see."

More Javanese had to be brought in for work on the road and also in preparation for land clearing. Living quarters for them were built in the village. Carpenters in Java, for some reason, were always Chinese. A gang of them arrived and set to work.

The big, slow buffaloes dragged tree trunks into the village where the Chinese workmen cut them into boards and joists with long, two-man handsaws. Their activities, though exceedingly slow, provided us with something to watch and we would stand and look at them by the hour.

Unlike the *Orang Javas*, the Chinese didn't ignore our interest. They were openly curious about us and as openly friendly and responsive. Among themselves too, they were unlike the Javanese because their work was enlivened by shouts, laughter, jokes, and probably curses. All in Malay, of course, and with a strong Chinese accent. They poked and punched each other in anger or in fun; despite their reputation for impassivity they were regular extroverts compared with the Javanese.

After the Chinese, along with their jokes and horseplay, had finally gotten up the frame of a long, barrack-like structure, the Javanese took it in hand and quickly covered it with bamboo and roofed it with palm thatch.

88

Meanwhile the Chinese leisurely moved on to begin the framework of another barracks.

As their dwellings went up, workers or coolies arrived from neighboring villages and countryside. They came on foot and brought not only their families, dogs, chickens, and goats but also all of their household goods; water jugs, rice baskets, cooking braziers, and bundles of sleeping mats and clothing.

By September, with the increased labor supply, the great day came when the blue bay was sighted through the trees. Dad, of course, had persisted in hacking his way the entire distance. Then a dock was built and the first boat put in at what Klaut grandly named the Port of Daringo.

After some tracks were laid, the ship's derrick set a tiny locomotive on the dock. The ship had also brought wheels and frames for small flatcars which were completed on the spot. By the time the tracks were laid up to the village, an engineer for the tiny locomotive was supposed to have arrived. Instead, came a letter saying that he was detained.

No matter, said Klaut, as there was nothing at the dock just then which had to be brought up to the village. But Dad with his own locomotive was like a little boy who couldn't wait for Christmas. His train was set up and he just had to run it right away. He didn't know how to drive a locomotive, even a miniature one, but he was a good mechanic and soon found out.

He was all ready to start off when Klaut stopped him. Dutch ceremoniousness came to the fore. The opening

89

of a railway line was a great event and its first run should be celebrated by a gathering of people with flags, flowers, and speeches. That was the proper way to do it.

After some persuasion, Dad agreed to the idea. He climbed—it was really only a step for his long legs—out of the locomotive and rode home on his pony. Next morning, he returned to the shore. The boys, of course, were mad about our train and dying to be aboard on its first trip so they went with him.

At the village a holiday was declared and everyone was told to assemble and to be dressed in his best. No flags were available except the big American one which Klaut said would not be right for the occasion. But the crowd held aloft paper lanterns, branches, and flowers. Mijnheer Klaut had donned his white ducks and stood ready to make a speech. Mevrouw Klaut had done her part by giving a small girl a bunch of flowers which was to be presented to Dad with another congratulatory speech.

Everything had been arranged, everything thought of except one crucial point. The Daringo people and others from equally remote regions had never seen a train before.

"Toot, toot," went the little locomotive somewhere deep in the jungle. The *Orang Javas* looked at each other in surprise. What could be making that strange noise? The locomotive, still tooting, chugged into sight. Now, everyone knows that the jungle is full of spirits— evil ones that lurk in the shadows. Here was an evil spirit—a big black one—coming toward them, staring

90

with its baleful eye, its iron teeth bared, tooting and blowing its fearsome breath.

With one accord the *Orang Javas* turned and fled.

When the train came to a halt, only the Klauts, Mother and I, and the worldly-wise Chinese were holding our ground. Maintaining his dignity, Mijnheer Klaut stepped forward. Gravely and at great length, he congratulated Dad on the opening of the Daringo Railroad. Mevrouw Klaut picked up the flowers the little girl had dropped in her flight. She handed them to Dad and made another speech. Mother and I feeling we should do something too, each gave Dad a kiss. When they got off the train our boys shouted "Rah! Rah! Rah!" The Chinese shouted after them, "Wah! Wah! Wah!"

The *Orang Javas* had fled as far as possible without going into the jungle. Who knew? Another fearsome monster might soon emerge from it. As to the monster which had appeared, they eyed it fearfully. It was not, as they had expected, devouring the people who stood near it. And Dad and the boys seemed to have ridden unharmed on its back.

Some of the bolder spirits cautiously approached and Dad called to them encouragingly. He patted the locomotive as though it were a horse and shouted: "See, it doesn't bite!" But even the bolder spirits were not sure about it and drew no nearer.

Now Dad and particularly the boys were ready for another ride. The Klauts, Mother and I, and the Chinese wanted a ride, also. We sat on the flatcars, well back so as not to fall off, and away we went.

We had been to the shore before, having ridden down on ponies when the road was first opened. But this was different, speeding along on a train! The jungle was beautiful now, I thought. An easy method of loco-motion is necessary to the enjoyment of nature. If you have to plow through it slowly and toilsomely, you can't put your mind on it.

The shore, a gleaming white crescent around the sapphire bay, was lovelier than ever. We saw it now as a romantic strand bordered by swamps of mangrove as tortured and twisted as a witches' wood. We strolled at the water's edge where pink coral reefs were awash with azure and green foam. The Chinese strolled after us prosaically gathering sea slugs, like foot-long caterpillars, which they would take home for dinner.

As we had ridden away on the monster's back and had returned unscathed, some of the Javanese dared to first approach and then to try a ride on it. They huddled on the flatcars holding each other tight and even adat couldn't keep them from screaming at the top of their lungs. It was terrifying but exciting and fun. Others ventured and soon the train never made a trip to the shore without a full cargo of Javanese. As the cars re-turned to the village loaded with supplies, the pas-sengers had to walk the four miles home. But a ride in the *kerata api-api*, carriage fire-fire, was worth it.

The train did more than provide joy rides. Another ship came in and brought materials for a gasoline-driven sawmill. The mill also seemed a fearful monster but it stayed in one place and ate only logs. Watching it eat logs came to rival train riding as a diversion and there were people there all day long.

Someone of an inquiring turn of mind wondered if it could eat anything besides wood so the man laid a metal bar on the carriage. Everyone was delighted when, with a horrible shriek and shudder, the great round saw came to a stop. After that the foreman had to keep reminding people that it was strictly forbidden to feed the saw.

Land clearing had already started but Dad felt it would not really get under way until he had bulldozers and some trucks. But he discovered that it was not only Klaut and the *Orang Javas* who didn't care for machinery. The government also frowned on it because it threw people out of work. So two bulldozers were all that Dad was allowed to bring in along with several trucks.

With what he had, Dad went right to work. He drove one bulldozer up from the dock on the road that had been leveled beside the railroad track. He expected Klaut to drive the other. But Klaut didn't. It wasn't that he couldn't manage a bulldozer. It just wasn't proper for an overseer to drive anything but a pleasure car.

Klaut assured Dad again that no *Orang Javas* would ever be able to learn to drive anything. Dad assured Klaut that they would. He picked out several likely lads and took them for rides in a truck. They at first screamed and huddled but then they liked it and soon they loved it. Dad succeeded in teaching them to drive. They learned fast and drove as rapidly as the terrain would allow. Their job was to haul felled timber to a pile where it could be burned or to bring logs to the sawmill. When they drove at high speed with their load of logs along the village paths, the villagers were, very rightly, afraid of them.

One of the lads was taught to operate a bulldozer which he drove as fast as a bulldozer was able to go. The chauffeurs, as they were called, loved their machines. But they never learned to remember that their pets had to be fed oil, gas, and water and be put under the shed at night.

Dad fumed because he had only two bulldozers. Lack of machines would double, treble, quadruple the time required for clearing. Although by October, over a thousand coolies were employed, the work was proceeding at the rate of only about three hundred acres a month. To Dad it was going at a maddening snail's pace.

But we could see the jungle gradually recede. Day after day the great trees crashed to lie like fallen giants until they were dry enough for burning. Then acrid smoke rose in columns and hung motionless in the air. When it cleared we saw rough, blackened stubble which remained hot and smoking for days. That blackened stubble, we felt, was *our* land and we were glad to see the jungle being gradually pushed back to make room for us.

13

"I SHOULD think we could build our house now," Mother said.

She had said this many times before. First, when the carpenters had arrived but, of course, the coolies' barracks had to be built first. Then when the sawmill had begun to eat logs and turn out piles of gleaming new boards, Mother insisted that some of them could certainly be used for our house.

But Dad remembered the terms of his lease and provided for medical care by building a six-bed hospital. And shortly after that burly, genial, young Doctor Klopper arrived to take charge there. Then education was given its due by the erection of a schoolhouse. A market shed was required as the Daringo population had grown from several hundred to several thousand. Next came a small structure which Klaut called the Administration Building. It contained an office for Dad, one for Klaut, and one for a future accountant and paymaster. Dad, busy with his bulldozer, spent little time in his office and Klaut was there only on payday.

"Now you certainly can't think of anything else that has to be built, can you?" Mother asked.

Dad said that he really should build a jail. As proprietor of Daringo he had been made a magistrate. Along with the Headsman and the Mohammedan priest, he was responsible for maintaining law and order. A police force of six *Orang policeys* had been formed. They wore splendid, blue serge, brass-buttoned uniforms but as they couldn't get around with shoes on, they went barefoot and they wore their impressive helmets rakishly on top of their turbans.

They strolled around the village in pairs and holding hands. Dad couldn't decide whether they held hands for mutual protection or through affection but it looked very unbusinesslike to him. He told them severely that in America the policemen never, never held hands.

Mother remarked that as the *policeys* had not yet caught any malefactors, Dad could surely put off building the jail until he had someone to put in it. Doubting perhaps that the *policeys* would ever catch anyone, Dad agreed that now at last we could start building our own house.

Mother had great plans for it. She sketched them with a stubby pencil on a sheet of notepaper. That, she told Dad, was what she wanted the house to be like. Dad, glancing at the confusion of lines on the paper, said perhaps Mother had better explain.

"Well, I want it to be like this . . ." Mother made vague gestures in several directions. "You know, with columns in front—" Another vague gesture— "You go into the hall, a big hall with a fanlight over the front door. . . . You know . . ."

"Not yet," said Dad. "But go on."

Mother went on and it finally became more or less clear that what she had in mind was a large southern colonial mansion. It would be just right for the climate, she said.

Dad agreed that it would suit the climate well enough. But the Chinese carpenters were so unfamiliar with the colonial style that he didn't think they could build a southern mansion. Besides, we couldn't take a great deal of time over our house as there were others to be built. Ours would have to be a small house and simple—no columns.

"And no staircase?" Mother asked dolefully. "I wanted a staircase . . . you know . . . like this. It comes down from the top . . ."

"Naturally," said Dad.

"Then there's a landing with a grandfather's clock on it. I saw a staircase like that in a picture once and it was just beautiful. On the landing was a bride. She was coming downstairs with her veil spread out . . . you know . . . like this. I've always thought of Charlotte coming down some stairs like that on her wedding day."

Dad said it made a charming picture. Then, drawing a deep breath, he explained that as we were living in the earthquake zone a two-story house would be dangerous. Besides, we didn't have a grandfather's clock. As for a bride, since I was only fourteen, the Strykers wouldn't be having one for quite a while yet.

Dad sat down and drew a plan himself. He showed it to Mother but she couldn't understand his neat, businesslike drawing any more than he had understood her scrawl. Fortunately for her dream of a mansion, Mother couldn't tell what the house would be like until it was almost completed. The roof was up before Mother grasped the fact that there were only four bedrooms. She said that four bedrooms were not enough but Dad said it was too late to make any changes.

But Mother insisted on a dining room. She must have a dining room with a bay window. Dad gave in on that but didn't add another room, he merely had the large living room divided by a partition. Mother complained that it was square and she hated a square dining room because there was no room for a sideboard. And where, she wanted to know, was the bay window? But by that time the carpenters were at work on a house for the Klauts.

Mother pondered as to whether or not a sideboard could be squeezed into the square dining room. She was also giving consideration to the style of the dining-room furniture. Meanwhile the carpenters were knocking together some rough chairs, tables, cupboards, and chests of drawers. When they were moved into the house along with seven narrow metal beds, our furnishing was completed.

Mother, looking about her new home, said she would have to see what she could do about it. But, as it turned out there was nothing she *could* do about it. The raw boarding of the walls and ceilings could not be painted because paint would not dry indoors in the damp climate. Nothing could be done about the furniture as varnish or polish would not dry either. The only thing

98

Mother could do was to get a set of rattan furniture to make the living room a little more comfortable. As to the treasures she had collected from the Arabs, she regretfully agreed with Dad that they should remain in storage in Batavia.

After our cramped quarters at the inn, our house, though no southern mansion, was comfortable enough with its big rooms and shady front and back porches. In the kampong at the rear were the godown, servants' rooms, the kitchen, and the bathroom. The tin tub in the bathroom was supplied with water brought from the river. In conformance with the government's regulations, we had a latrine, a well-built two-holer with a crescent cut in the door.

With the house came the servant problem. At least down here, Dad said, we would be able to get along with less than before. It seemed at first that we would have to get along without any. No one could be found who had been a house servant before.

Finally a village woman timidly volunteered to be our cook. She said apologetically that she knew how to cook only rice but would try to learn to cook other things. But she couldn't learn to cook other things. Our supplies from home were there but the cook was afraid of cans and jars—something might jump out at her. Mother knew how to cook other things but she couldn't do so on the floor over a brazier, so we continued to subsist mainly on rice.

When a man named Sito turned up and said he had worked as a cook in Wazi, Mother was glad to hire him.

Sito proved to be a good cook and even learned to deal with corn flakes and other delicacies. He was also efficient at serving the meals.

But it was then, when Sito was in the dining room, that we first noticed something strange about him. He stared at us with the most disconcerting intensity and followed our every move and gesture with really painful concentration. While he did so he mouthed and mumbled to himself in a very peculiar manner, rather as though he was eating and talking just as we were. Sito made Dad nervous. He tried to ignore his mouthings and mumblings, but couldn't help looking at him. The more Dad looked at him, the more Sito stared back like a conjured rabbit.

One evening after a long, hot day with the bulldozer, Dad lost his temper. He jumped up, threw down his napkin and said, "Sito, *stop staring!*"

Sito, still staring, threw down the napkin he had on his arm and said, "Sito, *stop staring!*"

"Why, the man's crazy," Dad shouted.

"The man's crazy," echoed Sito.

I was a little frightened but the boys were delighted with this unusual development. They all giggled. Peter let himself go, put his napkin over his mouth and shrieked with laughter.

Sito picked up his napkin from the floor, put it to his mouth and began to shriek, also. Peter stopped laughing and stared at him, a little frightened. Sito stopped laughing and stared back at Peter, also looking a little frightened.

After Dad had taken Sito to his room and locked the door, he went to Mijnheer Klaut. Klaut said that Sito was *latta*. Being *latta* is a mental aberration peculiar to the Far East. Those afflicted are normal at most times but when in new surroundings or with strange people, they feel an overpowering impulse to imitate others.

We were new and strange to Sito but he had fought down his impulsion as best he could. However, when Dad had shouted at him, his fit had come on irresistibly. Klaut said it would pass off. But next morning when Dad said in his gentlest tone, "Good morning, Sito. I hope you're feeling better," Sito, in the same solicitous tone, repeated his words.

After that, Sito returned to normal for several days. Then, as Mother sat sewing, she saw Sito in a corner of the room going through the gestures of hemming a skirt in thin air.

"Well," said Mother, "I don't mind that."

But a few days later when Mother was at her dressing table, Sito came and stood beside her. He took the brush from her hand and removing his turban, began to brush his long black hair. Mother *did* mind that, so Sito was fired.

Remembering the efficient and thoroughly sane cook we had had in Batavia, Mother wrote Juffrouw to ask if she could locate her. Juffrouw replied saying that the cook was willing to come to Daringo and would be there within a week.

We expected further word in regard to her arrival as

Dad planned to send someone to meet her at Wazi. But the cook walked from Wazi and turned up unexpectedly—and not alone. Her husband, Boy One, had come because, he said, he didn't think she should make the trip all by herself.

Boy Two had accompanied them because he liked us so much. He had brought his wife Sora so she could delouse him and roll his cigarettes. Manisan had come because she wanted to see her dear little children again. Chauffeur explained that he just felt like making the trip.

Dad said it was nice of them to come but we didn't need so many servants now. Only a cook. Didn't we need a Boy One also, asked Boy One. Dad said, "Well, perhaps . . ." And Mother said, "Yes, certainly."

Manisan repeated that she loved her little children dearly but Dad replied that the boys were too big to need a nurse, so Manisan volunteered to do the housework and washing. Then Dad decided to keep Chauffeur who would be useful with one of the trucks.

Smiling sweetly, Boy Two remarked that he would like to remain also. But, Dad asked, now that we had no sideboard for him to lean on, what would he do? Boy Two looked thoughtful, then brightening, said he could be our gardener. When Dad said we had no garden Boy Two replied that he would make us a garden, a perfectly beautiful one!

Of course Sora remained and made herself useful with the vegetables when she could take time from her attendance on Boy Two. Manisan soon found that she needed an assistant and found one in the village, a pretty little girl named Saritita.

So there we were, Dad said, with six servants which he felt were too many. But they all had jobs to do and did them, all except Boy Two. He explained that he was planning our beautiful garden. He did his planning lying on his back under a tree, playing a flute. Around him our yard began to grow wild and show every sign of rapidly reverting back to jungle.

14

MIJNHEER KLAUT was not inclined to hurry things. But he said that the work of clearing should be speeded up as much as possible before the rainy monsoon began. Dad thought that although rain would interfere with the burning of timber, the work of felling and cutting could go on anyway.

For a while, yes, said Klaut. But by midwinter when the real rains came, he was not so sure. He pointed out that when we arrived in Java in the spring we had seen only the end of the wet monsoon. No one had seen real rain, he said, until he had lived through a Java winter.

Mevrouw Klaut also had the weather on her mind and anxiously scanned the pale, burning sky where there had been no clouds for months. She wanted to be settled in her new home before the rains began. As the first of November approached, she kept her fingers crossed. Then, after her furniture was moved in, she said: "All right, let it come!"

As though Mevrouw's crossed fingers controlled the elements, it did come and that very afternoon. At two o'clock precisely the fiery sun disappeared. From low purple clouds rain fell as though poured from buckets and clouds of steam rose as it hit the hot ground.

After two hours, it ceased as suddenly as it had begun. The purple clouds rolled away and the sun shone out as bright as ever. Every day, after that, the shower began at two and ended at four as if by clockwork.

As the rain more or less coincided with the carpenters' siesta hour, it didn't interfere with the building of two more new houses. One for the accountant, who was soon to arrive, and the other for an assistant overseer, both of whom were married. Doctor Klopper, a bachelor, would continue to reside at the inn.

Ours, the Klauts', and the two other houses looked very spruce with their white paint (which would dry *outdoors*) and their red tile roofs. The inn looked shabby beside them and was improved by the addition of a large living room and new front porch. When the path from the village had been extended to the houses, Dad thought that a little landscaping was called for.

He roused Boy Two from his flute playing and said that now he meant business, Boy Two must really get to work. Boy Two bestirred himself languidly with a scythe and managed to keep the grass and weeds around the houses from growing higher than people's heads. But his plans for a beautiful garden remained forever incomplete.

Mijnheer Aken, the accountant, was dark and very earnest behind his thick glasses. His wife was equally dark and equally earnest. She was also talkative, much given to superlatives and could laugh or cry at the drop of a hat.

Mijnheer Assistant Overseer Vos and his wife, next to arrive, were a young, thin, blond pair who looked like brother and sister. Newly out from Holland, they seemed dismayed by life on the jungle's edge, but they said nothing about it. During the entire time we knew them, neither of them spoke a single word that was not strictly necessary.

But another and, to us children, more important arrival was expected. We were to have a governess. With the coming of fall, Dad and Mother remembered the good old days when we went to school and weren't underfoot all day long. They began to give serious thought to our education. We would be in Java for a long time—until the plantation was well started and in good working order. In moments of depression, Dad would groan that God only knew how long that would be. Too long, at any rate, for us to go without schooling.

Dad wrote to the American consul in Batavia to ask if there happened to be any stray American school teachers in Java. The consul replied that there were few Americans of any sort or description and none of them were teachers. There was, however, a stray English-woman named Miss Blue.

Mother wrote to Miss Blue, who replied that she would take the job although she had never been em-ployed by Americans before. Her previous employers had been the Tootler-Murfins, a very distinguished English family of British North Borneo. Miss Blue did not state why she had left the Tootler-Murfins but she implied that the young Tootler-Murfin's governess must certainly be good enough for anyone.

When we heard about the impending Miss Blue, the boys and I were bitterly disappointed. We had hoped that our parents wouldn't be able to devise any method of continuing our education at Daringo. We felt that they had outwitted us and we were mad about it.

However, when we became somewhat reconciled to the idea, we were curious about Miss Blue. We were all agog when she and Dad, who had gone to meet her at Wazi, rode up the path from the village.

Miss Blue, we saw, didn't wear an explorer's costume but a long, full-skirted white dress and a large hat with pink roses and a nodding blue ostrich plume. She was a tall, rawboned woman with a deep voice. As she stepped onto the porch, she remarked that the place was far more primitive than she had been led to expect. She looked severely at Mother who hastened to apolo-gize for not having described sufficiently our primitive-ness in her letter.

We had been curious to see Miss Blue. But merely seeing her was enough. We didn't like her and knew that we never would. At her remark about primitiveness, the boys and I pricked up our ears hopefully. Perhaps Miss Blue would mount her pony and ride away. Instead, she said in a foreboding and sepulchral voice that she would like to be shown her room. After that, she would be ready for her tea.

Miss Blue was to share my room. When she and her luggage had been put into it, Mother said nervously that she hoped Miss Blue would like the room and not mind having a roommate. As Miss Blue appeared at the bedroom door the boys and I hoped she would say she wouldn't be able to put up with such poor accommodations. But she had on her purple silk kimono and asked to be shown the bathroom. Mother led her to it, apologizing for the tin tub and the latrine out in the yard.

Ready for her tea, Miss Blue wore a ruffly dress a little more elaborate than her traveling costume. It was also white and tied with a pale blue satin sash and trimmed with lace insertions.

Like most women in the Far East, Miss Blue's clothes were out of date. But hers were much further out of date than any we had seen. Miss Blue must have left England a very long time ago or else was particularly insistent in clinging to the modes of her girlhood. Back in those far-off days, apparently, girls had dressed like sweet young things. And that was Miss Blue's style—red, bony, and weatherbeaten though she was.

Over her tea Miss Blue again complained of our crude way of life and also said that she didn't care for Ceylon tea. Hereafter she wished to be served with the

Chinese variety. Her tea finished, she proceeded to tell us all about herself. Only she hadn't much to tell. As a governess, the poor thing had passed her life in other people's houses and had not much life of her own. So she talked principally about her employers, the most important of whom by far, we gathered, had been the Tootler-Murfins of British North Borneo. Mr. Tootler-Murfin was a magistrate and a very, very important person.

Jim, already antagonistic, couldn't resist telling the governess that Dad was also a magistrate.

"Ah," said Miss Blue, turning to Dad. "Then perhaps, Mr. Stryker, I will be able to give you some pointers. I am familiar with the duties of a magistrate and you may come to me at any time for advice."

Even if he had felt he needed Miss Blue's advice, Dad didn't have to ask for it because she gave it copiously, freely and unasked. Not only in the field of law and administration but on all other subjects as well. She told Mother just what was wrong with the way the house was run and suggested many changes, quoting as authority the Tootler-Murfin house in North Borneo.

Miss Blue was also able to tell Mother just what was wrong with us. Apparently, everything was wrong. We had been so mismanaged from the very beginning that she doubted that at this late date she would be able to bring us up to the standards of the young Tootler-Murfins.

Besides her particular comments and criticisms, Miss Blue had a permanent bone to pick with us—she deplored our American accent. As our governess she conceived it to be her duty to try and teach us to talk in the British manner. She apparently thought that as long as she was about it she might as well try to improve our parents' accent also, so she frequently gave them pointers on pronunciation.

Dad and Mother were very meek with Miss Blue. Mother, because she was meek with everyone, even the cook. Dad wasn't at all meek but neither was he used to disagreeable women. He just didn't know how to deal with Miss Blue.

We had our lessons in the dining room and with the five of us Miss Blue had her hands full. We were sure that Peter had known how to read before he left Roselawn but he seemed to have forgotten all about it. Miss Blue had to start him off from the letter *A*. As Frank was six, he was ready for the letter *A* also, but since Peter was older his reading had to come first. Frank and Henry sat in a corner and played jacks while Miss Blue worked on Peter.

When she found time Miss Blue took up arithmetic with Jim and me. We found that we could argue about a British versus an American accent even while doing long division but we went no further than that in any event. Miss Blue was vague about what came after long division and Jim and I weren't anxious to find out. Instead, Miss Blue began to teach us French, but French was no fun because we couldn't argue about it. We had to take Miss Blue's word as to how it was pronounced.

15

AMONG Miss Blue's many suggestions in regard to Mother's housekeeping, none was more frequent than the remark that the godown door should be kept locked. Because a warning to lock the godown had been Juffrouw's parting shot, Miss Blue's remarks made some impression on Mother. But thinking the matter over, she decided that it was too much trouble to dole out food for each meal. Besides, she would be sure to lose the key, anyway.

Mother felt that Juffrouw's doubts about her becoming a real Dutch housewife were unfounded. Mother was as mild as milk but she imagined herself to be quite stern with the servants. But Mother was less stern than she imagined. The servants liked working for us and seemed to be settling down to stay because they began to send for their families to come to Daringo.

Boy One's parents arrived, both incredibly old, bent and almost indistinguishable because the old woman was as bald as her husband. They slept in the room with Boy One and Cook. Crowded as it was, Boy One found room for their daughter and her six-year old son who soon joined them.

Though Chauffeur's job was driving a truck, he had

a room in our kampong. His wife, Teena, and their three children all managed to squeeze into it. Chauffeur's youngest was a fat toddler of fifteen months. He had not been weaned as the Javanese do not wean their children entirely for several years, but he was old enough to eat solid food. His mother took him on her lap and stuffed small balls of rice into him. This went on until his belly-string was tight. Then, to bring him to the bursting point, he was put to the breast.

Though the Javanese children are weaned late, they begin to smoke early. The toddler's brother was three and already liked a cigarette from time to time though he had not yet lost his taste for mother's milk. When little brother's turn was over, he would suck for a little while, then light up and stroll off puffing.

Though Teena's baby was plump and vigorous, Mother was sure he was not well fed on only rice and milk. She handed the child's mother a bottle of cod liver oil and said that he should be given some every day. We didn't know whether or not Teena applied the oil to her child internally. But she certainly used it herself —externally—for hair oil—and could be smelt a block away.

Now Manisan said she was heavy-livered with longing for her husband, Apo. When Apo arrived he proved to be a wizened little fellow who seemed a meager mate for the buxom Manisan. Apo said that as he knew Manisan had such a fine large room (it was all of eight feet square) he had decided to bring along his young sister Fatima.

Boy Two had an aged father who arrived with four very young children. Boy Two was their father but Sora was much too old to be their mother. Boy Two, we decided, must have had a younger wife at some time or other.

Little Saritita explained that she was not an orphan, but her parents lived in a faraway village. Also, she added significantly, her father was a well-to-do farmer. He did not need to come and eat other people's rice. She had, however, an aunt and uncle in the village who were frequent callers and, as it happened, just at mealtimes.

So, with one relative and another, there was quite a crowd out in our kampong. Those who couldn't squeeze into the bedrooms spread their sleeping mats on the porch. Miss Blue pointed out to Mother that though the relatives needed only mat space at night, they were all eating three meals a day out of our godown.

Mother replied that they ate only three cupfuls of rice a day. What did that amount to? Miss Blue said that it would amount to quite a lot. Mother vaguely agreed with her and thought that some time or other she would figure it out. But was it worth bothering about? Besides, all of the relatives seemed to be happy living with us and Mother liked people to be happy.

On the kampong porch there was always a jolly crowd playing cards, smoking, chewing betel, and picking lice. Boy Two abandoned his post under the tree and sat regaling them with his flute all day long. Chauffeur seemed to be able to take time off to sit around also. Needless to say, the dashing fellow sat and flirted with

Fatima who was the prettiest girl on the place. There were enough children about for our boys to start a baseball team. Though they played with a tennis ball and a stick, they seemed to love it.

Besides our steady boarders there were many visitors from the village. Some came merely to sit and chat. Boy Two's father had a fighting cock and many came to pit their cocks against him. Those were merely minor league fights. Big fights between champions were held on the village square at night.

Then there were cricket fights. Manisan's little husband Apo was quite a hand with crickets, perhaps because he was so much like one himself. The crickets were trained to fight by being teased with a small paintbrush. When they had been brought to a frenzy by the brush, they were thrown into a bowl of water. After they had struggled until exhausted, they were calmed by being hung up by a thread. Then they were put in little bamboo cages and trained to leap at their opponent the moment the tiny, sliding door was opened.

Catching crickets was quite a business too. Of course, they were plentiful but real champions must be caught at night, in the full of the moon. It was Manisan herself who went out to catch crickets because on one midnight hunt Apo had had a dreadful experience. He had been kissed by a *pontianak*—the ghost of a girl who has died a virgin. Deprived of love in life, the ghost seeks it after death. At night the *pontianak* lurks under a waringin tree singing and combing her long black hair. When a man is lured by her song she kisses him. And her kiss is death unless the man is able to pull out one of her long black hairs.

Fortunately, Apo had managed to snatch a hair. So he had not died but only gotten a horrible fright. It served him right, Manisan said, for chasing after girls. He would have known she was a *pontianak* if he had only taken time to look. A *pontianak's* feet are always turned around backward because she walks toward death.

No women are imperiled by *pontianaks*. The only evidence they have of their existence is when their husbands come home with a long black hair that has to be explained. Have our American men, with their vaunted superiority, ever been able to think up a story as good as that?

Boy Two, perhaps grown bored with his fluting, came to ask Dad for a week's holiday. Dad granted it gladly and added that Boy Two need not return. Boy Two merely grinned at that. At the end of a week, still grinning, he returned with a young girl whom he took to Mother.

"*Nonya Besar,*" said Boy Two. "This is my wife."

"But isn't Sora your wife?"

"Oh, yes. But she's my old wife. This is my new one. We were married yesterday!"

Boy Two explained that *Tuan* Allah allowed a man to have as many as four wives. As a second wife was all right with *Tuan* Allah, Mother didn't feel she could object, but she wondered if Sora would. Sora didn't in the least; she seemed to like Wife Two and treated her as a younger sister. When poor old Sora could take time from her care of Boy Two's children, she meekly rolled the new wife's cigarettes and deloused her head for her.

There was no trouble on the score of Sora and Wife Two. But between Chauffeur's wife Teena and pretty young Fatima, there was. Not only did Chauffeur spend more and more of his time chatting with Fatima but it seemed he took many long, late walks with her in the evening. Teena objected and objected strongly. Her liver grew black with jealousy—and with fear.

What she feared came to pass. Chauffeur wanted to make Fatima his second wife. Teena refused. She wasn't old and ugly enough yet, she said, for her husband to have a right to a new wife. He'd have to wait awhile, that was all. And Chauffeur had to wait because he could not take a second wife without the consent of his first.

Some foolhardy fellows, it seemed, took a new wife when their old wives didn't want them to. But then misfortune always befell the new wife. Sometimes she met with an accident, often she just got sick and died. The outraged first wife saw to that. Wife One had a right to do away with her rival. In remarrying without her consent, had not her husband caused her to lose face? Had he not violated the rules of adat?

Though the prospect of marriage was put off into the indefinite future, Chauffeur and Fatima continued their daily tête-à-têtes and their evening strolls. Finally Teena could bear it no longer and asked Mother to send Fatima away. Mother didn't feel she could interfere in the matter and told Teena not to take things to her liver so.

"All men flirt a little once in a while," said Mother.

"Flirt," Teena laughed bitterly. "If that was all they did!"

Mother was sorry for Fatima. Still, how could she do anything about it? But as it turned out, something *had* to be done.

For one night there was a frantic pounding at our back door. Dad opened it to find Fatima, dishevelled, screaming and in a dreadful state. Doctor Klopper must come immediately. She had an awful stomach. Teena had given her poison!

Doctor Klopper came and found that Fatima *did* indeed have a stomach-ache. But it was only gas not poison!

Next day we found that Teena had threatened to poison Fatima with ground-up tiger whiskers. Pulverized tiger whiskers were a favorite method of disposing quickly and painfully of one's enemies and rivals.

Boy One, who was an authority on adat, was deeply disturbed about Teena's threats. He said that poisoning Fatima would not be adat. A first wife had a moral right to do away with an unwelcome second wife but after all, a man had a right to a love affair from time to time.

Dad had been vaguely aware of the Teena, Chauffeur, and Fatima situation but he was so busy he had not wanted to take time to deal with it. Now he felt he would have to, particularly as Mother urged him. "After all, you're a magistrate, dear. You must do something about this—a question of murder right in our own back yard."

While Dad was trying to decide what he could do about it, Miss Blue spoke up to say what *she* would do. Murder meant nothing to these people, she said. They were always poisoning each other. In this particular case there was nothing to get upset about. Teena had publicly stated her intention of murdering Fatima. Therefore, if she did so, there would be no difficulty at all in having the *policeys* arrest her. Also, Miss Blue added, the best antidote for tiger whiskers was cornstarch and water. Did Mother happen to have any in the house? Mother said she didn't have any cornstarch. Besides, she hoped things would not go that far.

Next morning Dad put a padlock on the godown door and gave Mother the key and told her to keep it. Our wide-open godown and unlimited supply of rice, Dad knew, was the cause of the influx of relatives. Cut off the food supplies and that would be the end of our troubles with jealous wives and erring husbands.

Dad was right. After it was seen that the godown was going to be kept locked, first one, then another of the relatives came to bid us a polite farewell. They had enjoyed staying with us a lot, they said, but now they somehow felt they might as well move along toward home.

The day after little Apo and pretty Fatima left, Chauffeur came and squatted respectfully in front of Dad.

"Tuan Besar," he said in a polite tone, "I'm tired of looking at your face."

Miss Blue, an old Borneo hand, was able to explain that Chauffeur wanted to give up his job. The Javanese thought it rude to tell their employers they didn't want to work for them any longer. It was much less wounding, they felt, to say they were tired of looking at them. Though Chauffeur was useful with the trucks, Dad had gotten rather tired of looking at him also. He paid him off and told him to depart.

Chauffeur left immediately, that very night, and did not take Teena and his children with him. When she awoke and found herself deserted, Teena came to Mother.

"Ado, ado, ado, Nonya Besar! What is to become of me and my three poor little children? My husband has left me to go live with Fatima. Oh, how foolish I was not to poison her when I had the chance! Because now my children have no father and they will starve."

Mother said that Teena and her children wouldn't starve. They could live in our kampong and eat our rice as long as they wished.

Boy Two, with his four children and aged father, felt he couldn't afford two wives now that he had to buy their rice himself. He would have to give up one of them. But which should it be? Deciding, like any other mental process, was hard for Boy Two. But at last he came to a decision. He would keep Sora. True, she was old and ugly, but of all the wives he had ever had, none could roll cigarettes or pick lice like Sora.

16

MIJNHEER KLAUT had been quite right about the weather. The two hours' rain of early fall had lengthened to an afternoon's downpour. Then, often it would rain all night and sometimes all day as well. When the sun shone it was as bright as ever but did not dry the ground which became dense, unyielding mud.

The great trees still were felled but could not be burned or moved. Entangled with ferns, vines, and undergrowth, they lay in a morass flecked in low-lying places with puddles and pools. Dad struggled like a Titan against the rain and the mud. But by December only fifteen hundred of his ten thousand acres had been cleared.

The rain was not cooling. The temperature remained above ninety—day in, day out, and night and day. We lived in a steaming miasma of heat that grew fungus in our shoes during the night. Our clothing broke out in spots and rotted before our very eyes. Each time the sun appeared, everything was rushed outside to dry but nothing ever did dry completely.

As though seeking refuge, armies of insects invaded the house. We put small cans of kerosene under the legs of cupboards and bureaus to try to save our clothing from the omnivorous ants and beetles. Our dozen or so geckos were joined by so many friends and relatives that they collided on the ceilings and fell with a thump on top of the mosquito-net frames. Manisan had her fill of the flying things that seemed to come right through the screens or to breed right on the spot.

Even a snake came in—only a tiny fellow—but of the coral variety and deadly poisonous. Boy One spied him under the table while we were having dinner. With seven pairs of legs thrust confidently under the table, one would expect Boy One to spring to action. He did so, in his own way and in strict conformance to adat.

It was rude—not adat—to interrupt our conversation so Boy One waited until there was a pause. Then he again waited until he happened to catch Dad's eye. He bowed and said he begged Dad's pardon but there was something he really should draw to his attention. *Tuan Besar* knew him well enough, Boy One went on, to know he would not disturb him about any trivial matter. But the fact was, there was a coral snake under the table. Just by Peter's foot, in fact.

Dad was up and had snatched Peter out of his chair in a second. In the same second, the rest of us were up and well away from the table. Then Dad killed the snake with the carving knife and threw it out of the window.

That night Mother and Dad sat up later than usual playing Russian bank, but when they were ready to go to bed, Boy One was still hovering about. He had another communication to make. The dead snake shouldn't be left just outside the window because its mate would probably come to find it. Boy One said it would be best to take it and bury it far away.

"Then why the hell didn't you do it before?" Dad shouted in English.

Boy One didn't know English but he caught the drift of the remark. He explained that it was not adat for him to interrupt the card game. Also, it was not proper for him to leave the house without the permission of the *Tuan*.

"That's what I'm up always against," Dad said as he stripped for bed. "Adat, custom, resistance to change, slowness, inefficiency. I feel I'm being bogged down in

it just as I'm bogged down in this damned, everlasting mud."

"And Christmas is coming too," said Mother with her usual apparent non sequitur, but she spoke to the point. We had been away from home for a year. Our plantation was hardly started and its completion was a long, long way off. Mother was adaptable and liked it well enough in Java, but she sensed Dad's dismay at the accumulation of time and money he was putting into his venture.

"Only fifteen hundred acres cleared," Dad muttered.

"It won't seem much like Christmas here," Mother said. Each in his own way was thinking of the same thing.

The Dutch do not make as much of Christmas as we do. They give and receive presents on Saint Nicholas' Day, early in December, so we celebrated our Christmas alone. In spite of fresh supplies and presents from home, it did not, as Mother said, seem much like Christmas.

Dad found a tree that was shaped something like a fir and had needles, but its needles were large, sparse and pulpy like those of a cactus. On Christmas Eve we decked it with ornaments we had brought from home. Then we stood around it and sang Christmas carols.

When we called in the servants and gave them presents, they were surprised and pleased. They were very intrigued with our tree and our singing. Boy One said he had not known that the *Orang Americas* had magic trees which they worshiped as the Javanese worshiped the waringins. He had thought, he said, that they worshiped *Tuan Yasu*, Lord Jesus.

Dad explained that we did worship *Tuan Yasu*. The tree and the singing were in honor of his birth. Boy One had heard about *Tuan Yasu* and knew he had lived on earth like any other *orang*. That was a funny thing, Boy One thought, for a god to do. He personally preferred a god like *Tuan* Allah who stayed where he belonged—up in the sky.

Immediately after Christmas, Dad had to make a trip to Batavia. He hated to take time out for it, to leave the work which he felt without him would bog down entirely, but he was planning ahead. No matter how little land was cleared by spring, a tapioca crop would have to be planted in May. When it was mature, a year later, the factory would have to be ready to process it. It would take a long time to build the factory. The first step was the erection of an electric power plant, the materials for which would have to be imported from the United States. So Dad was going to Batavia to order them immediately.

Mother was very anxious to go with him. She longed to have a comfortable stay at a hotel, to buy some clothes that didn't have spots on them and to get her hair waved. She thought that Miss Blue could run the house and look after the children in her absence. Miss Blue, however, informed her in no uncertain terms that she was not a housekeeper or child's nurse. So Mother had to stay at home.

Somehow, after Dad left, it seemed to rain harder

than ever. That night as we sat at dinner under the smoky oil lamp, the heat and dampness seemed more oppressive than before. We felt listless, out of sorts, and had little to say.

Mother went to bed early, soon after we did. She was careful about locking the heavy wooden shutters at all the doors and windows. One could hardly imagine that Miss Blue was nervous, but she went around after Mother to assure herself that everything was securely fastened. Between the two of them, it is certain that the house was tightly closed that night.

Next morning when Boy One, as usual, rapped on the back door Mother went to open it for him. Passing through the dining room, she saw that the shutters of the door onto the porch stood open. Boy One asked if *Nonya Besar* had remembered to lock them last night. Mother said she was certain that she had.

Then, said Boy One, someone had broken into the house. They had better look around to see if anything had been stolen. Nothing was found to be missing until Boy One began to lay the breakfast table. He discovered that all of the spoons were gone.

Miss Blue, sitting judicially over her China tea, was able to tell us just how the thief had gotten in. He had dropped a string with a hook on the end of it through the shutter opening and had lifted the latch. Then it had been easy to push open the screen door which had only a small bolt. These people, she said, were very ingenious at that sort of thing.

Mijnheer Klaut immediately started the *policeys* on

a search for our burglar. Off they set, hand in hand through the village to ask if anyone knew who the burglar might be. Or, failing that, had anyone happened to see some silver spoons around anywhere?

We were all quite thrilled about our burglary. We thought it was great fun—as long as daylight lasted. But that night, again one of heavy rain, we took a more somber view. The loss of the spoons was not very important, but the idea of someone breaking into our house made us uneasy.

Lying in the darkness, listening to the familiar night sounds, rain on the roof, a gecko on the wall, and the snoring of Miss Blue who shared my room, I thought about the person who had entered our house so quietly while we were all sound asleep.

Because of that perhaps I didn't sleep very soundly. I was awakened by an ordinary, familiar sound that I heard all day long without noticing it. A cupboard door creaked in the living room which was next to my bedroom.

The sound was not repeated. In the silence even the ordinary house sounds were hushed. I didn't hear them in the intensity with which I listened for another sound, another movement from the person I knew was in the next room. It was very quiet there in the inky darkness. Was the burglar also listening to hear if anyone had stirred when the door creaked? Or was he quietly going about his business at the cupboard where the cashbox was kept?

At the thought, I sprang out of bed. Then I paused,

because what was I going to do? Light the lamp, go in and confront the intruder? He might have a creese, one of those long, curved Javanese swords I had seen. He might even kill me. Or Mother and the boys might awaken and he might kill them.

I would stay right where I was, on guard and listening for any sound. What I would do if I heard another sound, I had no idea, but I heard nothing. Gradually, as my tension relaxed I began to hear noises, the usual ones always heard at night but nothing else. I became convinced the intruder must have left the house but even so, I must still stand guard and listen. A chair being handy, I decided to do my listening sitting down but I must not, dare not, go to sleep. I must keep watch— nothing must tempt me to lie down in bed.

At daybreak I awoke from peaceful slumbers and found that I had after all, lain down on the bed. It took me a few moments to even remember what had happened during the night. Had it been a dream? Had I only imagined the creaking of the cupboard door?

I dashed into the living room. The door shutters stood open, open too was the cupboard door, and the cashbox was gone.

After I had aroused the household, Miss Blue indignantly asked me why I had not awakened her. She would not have been afraid, she said, to go in and face the burglar. As a matter of fact, I had completely forgotten about Miss Blue. Even her snores, which had certainly continued while I was so intently listening, had not brought her to my mind. Obviously, I should have awakened her. If anyone could deal with an intruder singlehanded, it was the dauntless Blue.

When he heard the news Mijnheer Klaut insisted we must have a man in the house. That was entirely unnecessary, Miss Blue said. Just give her a gun; she had been the best pistol shot in Borneo and would be able to deal with the burglar if he ventured to return. Klaut was inclined to agree with her but nevertheless he arranged to have Doctor Klopper bring his revolver and spend the following night on our sofa.

The *policeys* were very apologetic about our second robbery and promised to try and do better next time. Klaut ordered them to stand guard around our house during the following night. They were to keep an eye on our kampong because Klaut was sure that one of our servants, who knew where things were kept in the house, must be the thief.

That night the *policeys* kept an eye on our kampong. Or perhaps, during the long watch, their eyes closed. For next morning it was discovered that someone had entered the inn, ransacked Doctor Klopper's room and taken all of his valuables.

17

MIJNHEER KLAUT rebuked the *policeys* and urged them to redouble their vigilance—or if they could not be vigilant, to at least try to keep awake. The inn was only a stone's throw from our house, so Doctor Klopper's valuables had been stolen right from under their noses.

Klaut had already had the *policeys* search our servants' rooms. Now, his own, the Akens', and the Voses' kampongs were examined too but with no better results. Klaut questioned everyone closely but learned nothing.

"And he never will," said Mevrouw Klaut. "None of them ever give information that will get an *Orang Java* in trouble with the *Orang Blandas*. The only way to deal with this business is as they themselves would—by magic. That's what you should try, Mevrouw Stryker, a little *guna-guna*."

"But I don't believe in magic," said Mother. "Do you?"

"Not in the least," replied Mevrouw Klaut. "But sometimes thieves are discovered by *guna-guna*. My servant tells me there is a magician in the village. If you like I'll get him to do some *guna-guna* for you. But you must promise not to let Albert know about it. He thinks it's not proper to have anything to do with Javanese magic."

As Mevrouw Klaut was so insistent, Mother consented to see what the magician could do. Because it was to be a secret from her husband, Mevrouw brought the magician to our house in the afternoon while Klaut was at work.

We Strykers didn't believe in magic or magicians either, but we had to admit that the magician Torat looked his part. He was a tall, thin old man with a sparse beard. Over his turban he wore a long cloak and

128

his turban was particularly tremendous. This was because he had made a pilgrimage to the sacred city of Mecca. Pilgrims to Mecca were endowed with special spiritual powers. As an outward sign of their inward grace, they were privileged to wear extra-big turbans.

Torat ordered everyone to assemble in the dining room. As he stood looking us over, the servants seemed awe-struck. And in spite of ourselves, we too were impressed by his *Arabian Nights* appearance.

"Now," said Torat, taking a small object from his waistband, "I need the help of some person who is absolutely pure."

He looked searching at the assembled faces which showed some embarrassment.

"I need an aged person whose passion is spent."

He looked at Miss Blue who was probably the oldest person present. At his glance Miss Blue gave a snort and flounced out of the room. We couldn't tell whether she was offended at his supposing her to be elderly or at his use of the word "passion."

Mevrouw Klaut was next in age after Miss Blue. Sora looked old enough to be her mother but the Javanese age quickly and Sora was probably younger. Mevrouw Klaut took Torat very seriously. She solemnly explained to him that she was living in the state of matrimony.

"Then," said Torat, "I must have a young and innocent child."

Our little brother Henry loved the limelight. At Torat's words he stepped eagerly forward. But Torat shook his head at the mischievous and light-hearted boy.

He said that Henry was young enough, but his was not the sort of nature to establish contact with the unseen powers. In Henry's stead, he chose the more sedate and thoughtful Frankie.

Torat held up the small object which looked like a piece of brownish putty. It was his magic beeswax that had grown brown from long use. Muttering something —spells or prayers—he put the dab of wax on Frankie's thumbnail.

"Look at it closely," Torat told him. "You will see someone in the wax. That person will be the thief."

Frankie looked attentively at his thumbnail for some time. Then he said he didn't see anything but a piece of wax. Now we knew Torat had been right in choosing Frankie instead of Henry. If Henry had been asked if he saw someone in a piece of wax, he would have been sure to say he did. He was a wonderful liar and would be able to describe the person right down to the length of his fingernails.

"The child sees nothing," said Torat. "Then I must make some little *orangs*."

At this there was a stir among the servants. Whether they were merely surprised as we were, or were moved by some stronger feeling, we couldn't tell.

"Bring me a pair of scissors and a sheet," Torat ordered Manisan.

When Manisan brought the sheet Torat laid it on the dining table and carefully folded it in a certain way, then he skillfully cut into it with the scissors and held up his handiwork. It was a row of little manikins all holding each other's hands—the sort of paper dolls we cut out for children.

"Now we must put the *orangs* in a safe place," said Torat, looking about.

He unlocked the china closet and removed all of the china from one shelf. He pinned the dolls to the back of the shelf using a great many pins—one in the head, belly, arms, and legs of each of them. There they stood, six of them in a row holding hands. Torat gave the key to Mother and told her to keep the closet locked.

"Now," said Torat, "whichever of the servants have been stealing will suffer as the little *orangs* do. They will get pains in their heads or bellies or arms and legs." Then, wrapping himself in his dark cloak, Torat stalked away.

Before she left our house Mevrouw Klaut enjoined us all to strictest secrecy. Albert must know absolutely nothing about any of this.

Ten minutes later Klaut came in. He had knocked off work earlier than usual because he had some padlocks he wanted to put on our doors and windows. When he saw the little *orangs* in the china closet, he said: "You are learning the customs of the country very fast, Mevrouw Stryker. So fast, that I suspect my good wife has been up to something."

Mother hastened to explain that it was all nonsense, of course. Naturally, she didn't believe in *guna-guna* at all. Klaut said he didn't either, but still, strange things happened sometimes. Much better not meddle with it.

With the good, strong padlocks on the doors and

131

good, strong Doctor Klopper asleep on our sofa, we felt safe and reassured—until sometime late that night. I had not been able to get to sleep so I went to Mother's room. She had not been able to sleep either and was reading in bed. I said I wasn't sleepy and would read for a while also, so I took up one of her detective stories and lay down on Dad's bed. But I didn't read and soon I was aware that Mother wasn't reading either.

"I wonder," said Mother, putting down her book.

"So do I." I knew what she was wondering about—Torat and his *guna-guna*. Was there anything in it? Only a short while ago we would have been positive there was not, but now we wondered. Not only about Torat's performance that afternoon but about Java itself, this land alien to us and perhaps inimical. Had we been wise to invoke its spirits? Was there perhaps really something in it? In the dark, quiet stirring of the night we were not sure.

Next morning we had forgotten those nocturnal fears. The padlocks were still fastened and Doctor Klopper roused from untroubled slumber on his sofa. All was safe, secure, and normal.

But breakfast was late so Mother went out to the kitchen to see what was the matter. Cook wasn't there and the fire had not been lighted. When Mother knocked at the door of Cook's room, Boy One appeared. He was in his underpants without his turban and his long hair hung down his back.

"*Sakit*," he moaned. "*Sakit, banyack sakit*. . . . Sick, much sick."

132

He had eaten something that disagreed with him, he said. Cook was sick also and neither of them would be able to do any work that day.

Fortunately Manisan volunteered to cook breakfast although she had cut her arm. It was all bandaged up and must have pained her because Manisan didn't have a word to say for herself all that morning.

With her bad arm, Manisan couldn't make the beds. It seemed that Saritita couldn't make them either as she was feeling poorly. Teena helped Mother and me with them and when we had finished we went to dust the living room. Glancing out of the window, we saw that Boy Two was limping so badly he could hardly get about.

"What's the matter with him?" Mother asked.

"*Sakit, banyack sakit,*" said Teena promptly. "All *sakit* but my three little children and me. Boy One and Cookie, Manisan, Boy Two, Saritita, and Sora—all *sakit!*"

Fearing an epidemic had broken out, Mother sent for Doctor Klopper to return. He arrived on the run and hastened to examine the servants. But there was nothing in particular the matter with them.

"Just lazy," the doctor said. "Tell them you will fire them if they don't get up and do their work."

Of course, Mother couldn't bring herself to do anything as harsh and unkind as that. Besides, she felt sure they would get better in a day or so.

But they didn't get better—they got worse. Next day, Manisan's arm was so sore that she had to stay in bed. Boy Two's leg was so bad he couldn't drag himself

133

around. Only Teena continued in health and helped us with the housework.

She went on with her refrain, "*Sakit, sakit* . . . all but my children and me. Remember, *Nonya Besar,* you told me I could eat your rice as much as I liked. When I took food from the godown, it wasn't stealing. Besides, Torat didn't make a little *orang* of me!"

Mother tried to ignore these insinuations. She didn't want to believe that the servants were sick just because the dolls had pins in them. Besides, Torat's magic was supposed to reveal the thief who had actually broken into our *house.* Probably all of the servants had pilfered food from the godown when it was unlocked but that was not really stealing.

In daylight at least, Mother didn't believe in *guna-guna* but she did believe in the powers of self-suggestion. Fortunately, she had not lost the key to the china closet. So on the third day of universal and *banyack sakit,* she opened it and took out the little *orangs.*

She carried several armfuls of newspapers out into the yard just by the kampong. When she came out with the first batch of papers, several of the kampong doors were opened. By the time she emerged with the *orangs* in one hand and a box of matches in the other, every door was open and all the servants were watching her.

Mother lighted the newspapers. When they were well ablaze, she threw in the *orangs.* They writhed for a moment as though alive, then blackened, crumbled, and disappeared. All of the doors closed as though shut by a single hand.

By afternoon, Boy One felt better and was able to serve tea. Cook also felt better and fixed dinner that night. Next morning Manisan was able to do the housework, helped by Saritita who had also recovered. Boy Two went off to his flute playing without a limp.

That afternoon Klaut came to bring us news. The police in Wazi had arrested our burglar. Chauffeur, who was living there now with Fatima, had felt in need of funds. To supply himself he had returned to our well-known premises. Then he had made the great mistake of trying to pawn our spoons and Klopper's watch in Wazi. He should have gone somewhere farther away where a description of the missing articles had not been given to the police.

18

WHEN Dad returned from Batavia, his news of his successful business transaction was quite overshadowed by our news about our burglaries. Dad was very upset at the idea of our having had such a scare. Mother and I admitted that we had been scared but the boys said they hadn't been frightened at all. They insisted that they would have killed Chauffeur with the carving knife if only they had not happened to be asleep at the time of his visits.

Dad immediately got back to his work of clearing the jungle which proceeded more slowly than ever because it rained continually. Not only was the atmosphere hotter and more drippingly wet now but our nerves began to crack under the strain.

People should pay attention to the weather. I mean not only by donning coats when it is cold and removing them when it is hot but also noticing the way bad weather can depress us. We should remember it is only the weather and not the bottom dropping out of the universe.

In the worst part of the rainy season, it would have been easy to be like Chicken Little and think that the skies were falling. Because it seemed they *were* falling, in blinding, thundering sheets, and that we would be crushed beneath them into the steaming, marshy ground.

Mother admitted that the rain got her down. Her lowest ebb, she said, was that night in January after a week of continuous downpour. It had cleared a little after dinner and everyone had gotten out his red waxed paper umbrella and plowed down to the square to see a cockfight.

Mother didn't care for cockfights so she stayed home and made me stay to keep her company. Miss Blue, as usual, had withdrawn to her room. Mother lay on the sofa, reading one of her interminable series of detective stories. I had one too but it wasn't very good. After an hour of trying to make my way through endless clues and complications, I grew bored. I put down the book and decided to go out to the kitchen to make some cocoa.

There was a dim light on the back porch where Manisan was sitting huddled close to the door. She said she had not gone to the cockfight because she felt out of sorts. She would be glad to make the cocoa and please, could she have some too in the living room with Mother and me because she was feeling so depressed and nervous.

"What do you feel nervous about?" I asked.

"Listen," said Manisan. "What do you hear?"

"Only the rain and something . . . the monkeys in the treetops. Or perhaps it's the wind."

"It's not the wind," said Manisan. "There's not a breath of air stirring. And it's not the monkeys either. It's ghosts, the souls of little dead children crying in the treetops. Listen, don't you hear them, *Nonee?*"

I listened, and I looked out beyond the dimly lighted porch into the inky blackness. It was so dense it seemed to move, to pulsate as though breathing. And there was a stir, a movement of some sort under the steady beat of the rain.

"But it's only what you always hear at night," I said.

"No," said Manisan. "Tonight it's different. It's little souls. I don't like it when the little souls cry. It makes my liver heavy. It means something is going to happen. Listen again, *Nonee,* and you'll hear them."

"I don't want to hear them," I answered crossly and then as I went back into the house I told Manisan to make the cocoa.

And in spite of her heavy liver and forebodings Manisan, sitting on the living-room floor, smacked her lips over the cocoa and said she would like another cup.

As she was pouring it, she stayed her hand to listen. The *gung-gung*, the hollow drum by the village gate, began to beat. It was sounded not only to welcome travelers but to beat out messages in a sort of wooden Morse code. It was used frequently during the day but we had never heard it before at night.

"What does it mean?" we asked Manisan.

She listened attentively all through the message. Her face became somber. "It says than an *orang* has gone *amok*."

When an *orang* felt the skies were really falling, when madness seized him and he took his creese to go out and kill any living creature in his path, the *gung-gung* sounded warning.

Manisan listened again as the warning was repeated. "It says he has killed in the village but they could not catch him. Now he has left the village and the *policeys* have gone after him. The *tuans* are searching for him also."

Manisan finished filling her cup. "It's a bad night. Something always happens when the dead children cry. I don't like it."

Mother and I didn't like it either. We sat very still to listen. When you listen intently, you hear—something—the wind in the treetops or a child's cry? A monkey stirring or was it a stealthy, naked footfall in the darkness?

Perhaps it was the beating of my heart or a throbbing

in my ears but I did hear something. Was it the sound of the sea? We were too far away for that. The sound was low, barely audible but it was close, all around us.

Mother heard it too, because she was white with fear. While we stared at each other, a spoon rolled from the table to the floor and our cups tinkled in their saucers. The light shifted because the lamp overhead was swinging gently to and fro. When we jumped to our feet we felt the floor tremble with the dull roar that seemed to roll under it like the sea.

I was seized with abysmal terror. I knew the earthquake could shake the house down on our heads. I knew the ground could open and swallow us. But my terror was not only of that. It was the terror of knowing that the earth could move out of its wonted course.

The dull roar rolled away to silence. The sounds of creakings and stirring from all over the house ceased and the lamp hung motionless. Manisan crawled out from under the sofa and said it had been only a tremble. The earth sighing in her sleep.

The *gung-gung* sounded again. Even Mother and I could tell it was pounding out a different message. Manisan listened. "The *orang amok* is dead. *Tuan Besar* has killed him."

Mother gave a shriek of laughter. Still laughing, she dropped into a chair and laughed with the tears running down her face. Her shrieks affected me and I began to laugh too, without knowing why I did so.

Manisan watched us gravely. The Javanese do not allow themselves the outlet of hysteria. Perhaps that is why every once in a while they have to take their knives and go out and kill.

A few minutes later we learned exactly what had happened. Dad had meant only to wound the *orang amok*. He and Klaut were cautiously lighting their way along a narrow path. Suddenly the man was before them—bloodstained, for he had killed three people in the village. He swung not a knife but a heavy wood-man's ax. Klaut had to take time to set down the lantern so Dad fired first. He was ashamed of himself, he said. He must have been rattled or he would have hit the man, as he intended, in the leg instead of in the chest.

Mother was ashamed of herself also. To go and have hysterics because of a slight tremble and because Dad had killed a madman! Later, explaining it, she said she thought she had been so jitttery because she was idle, bored, and had nothing to keep her busy.

People should pay attention to the weather. They should not blame its effects on idleness or anything else. An earthquake, even a slight tremble, shows that we live only for a moment and on sufferance between the earth and the sky.

If Mother had properly diagnosed her case—if she had blamed her jitters on the weather—she would not have written that letter to Macy's in New York. It was addressed to the buyer of the food department and asked if he wouldn't like to carry a line of preserved fruits. Exotic fruits, straight out of the Java jungle.

Fortunately, the buyer replied cautiously. If his answer had been enthusiastic, Mother would have carried out her plans on a large scale. Then who knows what might have happened to the people who ate the exotic fruits she would have preserved?

The buyer wrote that if he was sent a sample, a *very small* sample of the preserved fruits, he might consider giving her an order. But there was not much demand for jungle fruits in New York at that time.

Mother and I were disappointed at the buyer's cool reply. We were both convinced we must do something to keep from having the jitters and what could be better than putting up exotic fruits in attractive bottles and sending them first to Macy's and then, as the demand grew, probably all over the world.

"Try it out, anyway, in a small way," Dad said consolingly after he had read the buyer's letter.

We hated to begin in a small way instead of in a large one. But we had to have something to do right away, so we waited only long enough to get three dozen mason jars from Wazi.

Now we had to be patient till Sunday, when the men were not working. Then Dad took half a dozen coolies out into the jungle and told them to pick a basketful of all the fruits they were sure could be eaten without ill effect.

The men, who were being paid extra for Sunday work, picked enthusiastically. The baskets were soon piled with glorious fruit of crimson, purple, gold, and pink; some as big as watermelons, some small and bunched like grapes.

Dad wanted to sample them himself. He picked up a luscious-looking thing rather like an apple but purple.

"Don't eat that, *Tuan Besar!*" cried the coolies.

"Why not?"

"Because, *Tuan Besar*, it will make you turn green and die in convulsions."

"But what about the other fruit?"

They would not all make you turn green and die, the coolies said. Some would make you very sick and others only a little sick.

"But I told you to pick only edible fruits," said Dad.

The coolies knew that but, they said, since *Nonya Besar* was going to send them all the way to the land of the *Orang Americas*, what difference did it make if the fruit made people sick or not?

Dad hated to return empty-handed. He asked if *any* of the fruit could be eaten. Those pear-shaped, pink things called *jalas* were all right, the coolies said, though they were somewhat apt to cause gas.

When Dad came home with only one basket of fruit, Mother and I were bitterly disappointed. It was Mijnheer Accountant Aken who pointed out that most of the edible fruits were cultivated and did not grow wild. But *jalas*, he said, weren't bad though he too had found that they caused gas. But then, he added encouragingly, he was apt to be gassy anyway.

Our kitchen (until the demand grew) was the laboratory which had been recently added to the Administration Building. It had a cold water faucet, a worktable, and a coal stove. It was hot standing over the steaming pots of *jalas* when both the temperature and the humidity were well above ninety. Besides the heat *in* the the room, not a breath of air came from outside. The door and the windows were packed solid with *Orang Javas*. They were entranced at the sight of us losing face by doing physical work.

But when we finally ladled the *jalas* into the jars, they looked scrumptious. They had turned a deeper pink in their thick, syrupy juice. They tasted good also, though a little too sweet, perhaps. In our next batch, we would try using a little less sugar.

By the time we finished sealing our thirty-six jars we were very tired but well satisfied with our work. We discussed whether we should send the *jalas* right off to Macy's or wait until we had gotten some more attractive and artistic containers to put them in.

Mijnheer Aken had been away during the day so he went to his office in the Administration Building that evening to catch up on his accounts. He was roused by a pistol shot. It seemed to be right in the building. Then there was another shot, another and another—a regular volley. Had someone gone *amok* with a gun?

Mijnheer Aken took his revolver from his desk drawer and crept cautiously into the hall. The shots continued to ring out. They seemed to come from the laboratory and Mijnheer Aken carefully opened the door of the darkened room. Another shot—something hit him in the face. He put up a hand to wipe his glasses. His hand was

143

red and sticky. But Mijnheer Aken was not wounded, merely covered from head to foot with thick, sweet, pink *jala* juice.

19

AFTER the failure of our canning enterprise, Mother gave up and let the rain and weather have thir way. Idle and easygoing by nature, she was not one to struggle too hard against circumstance.

When our trunks had arrived from Batavia, Mother had been glad to abandon her explorer's costume and dress nicely again. But that had been months ago, before the rains came. Now she was in her sarong and waist all day and spent most of her time reading on the sofa.

Mevrouw Klaut and Mevrouw Accountant Aken dropped in occasionally for morning coffee or for afternoon tea. Mevrouw Assistant Overseer Vos, apart from a formal monthly call, did not appear at all.

Though constantly on hand, Miss Blue wasn't much of a companion. She had at first been extremely ready with her advice and suggestions. Mother had listened mildly but somehow just didn't get around to putting them into effect. So Miss Blue's comments had ceased. Mother just wouldn't take the white man's burden seriously. Obviously she was not of empire-builder stuff.

However, in the oppressive afternoon heat, even Miss Blue was glad to abandon part of her own burden. By mutual consent, we skipped our afternoon classes and all took a good long nap. After that, we went bathing in the river which was one form of activity that was not interfered with by the rain.

Like Mother, we became extremely negligent in our attire. The boys forgot all about shirts and wore only shorts. We went barefoot in the house and kept our shoes on the porch as Mother insisted on our wearing them out of doors through fear of hookworm. I wore only a sarong and looked, as Miss Blue frequently remarked, just like a native. But Miss Blue herself kept up her standard. She never left the house without her cotton gloves and her big hat, its blue plume sadly bedraggled but still bobbing genteelly.

At first Mother had struggled against Cook's tendency to feed us only *rijst tafel* but now she had given up on that point too. We had rice for lunch and dinner and sometimes for breakfast as well. We got used to it and liked it. Canned goods and similar delicacies had disappeared from our menu. Also things we had thought to be necessities such as bread and potatoes, beef and pork, and fresh butter and milk. Our provisions all came from the local market and Mother had forgotten about supplies from home. Her only importations now were cod-liver oil and fresh batches of detective stories.

Dad, on the other hand, *was* of empire-builder stuff. Despite tremendous difficulties, twenty-five hundred acres were cleared by March. In his sense of accomplishment, Dad almost forgot that he had expected to have half of his land cleared by that date. He thought only of the fact that the rains were abating and that the ground was finally dry enough for plowing. He had been able to import a number of tractor plows and to find lads who were ready to drive them.

But the work could not begin immediately. Adat ordained that breaking ground must be accompanied by a religious ceremony and a three-day general holiday. The earth, personified by the goddess Sri, must be placated before her breast was torn by the plow. Sri apparently objected to the use of even a hand plow and when those ruthless red tractors were to be used the ceremony of propitiation must be of especial solemnity.

Torat, the magician, was the man who knew how to deal with old Mother Sri. Dancing and beating his cymbals, he led a procession out to the fields. The priest, representative of *Tuan* Allah, was not present. To him, votary of the one true god, Sri was a mere pagan superstition.

When Torat's procession reached the spot where the tractors were ready to start work, he conducted a long and complicated rite to induce Mother Sri not to be angry when her children wounded her. She must forgive and forbear and mercifully reward their labors with a plentiful harvest.

We did not attend the ceremony as Klaut said the presence of unbelievers might be resented. However, after returning from the fields everyone celebrated in more mundane fashion by a good three days of making *ramee-ramee*, or merry-merry.

On the third day a great feast was held in the market shed. It was followed by a drama, or *wayang*, acted by some strolling players and the *Orang Blandas* were invited to attend.

Paper lanterns hung among the trees on the square where the entire population had assembled. In the center was the stage lit by kerosene lamps. Most of the throng were standing up but just in front of the stage was a row of chairs for the *Orang Blandas*.

After we were seated we looked around and spied in the crowd Boy One, Cook, and the rest of our servants. We of course said hello to them but they didn't reply. In fact they cut us dead. Apparently it was not adat for servants to greet their employers outside of the house. We didn't know it but they certainly did and stared past us like graven images.

The orchestra of about a dozen musicians was crouched just in front of us with its gongs and flutes, drums, horns, copper-bowl xylophones, and cymbals. Like the flutes we heard in the village and Boy Two's too familiar tooting, the music carried only a limited number of notes. It is not discordant like Chinese music but thin, repetitious and tends to become monotonous.

Soon the curtain of white sheeting was pulled back and the actors came onto the stage. They were masked and wore high, tiaralike headdresses and their silken sarongs were embroidered with gold or silver threads. The men were naked above the broad, velvet belts which held scabbards for their long, curved creeses. The women's silk scarves were wrapped around their breasts and hung down over one shoulder. They all wore a great deal of heavy, ornate and tawdry jewelry.

A man with a particularly high, gilt headdress came forward stepping on the balls of his feet, toes out and in cadence with the music. He held his arms and hands stiffly, with the fingers turned back as though he were double-jointed. When the music paused, he paused too and assumed an exaggerated pose. He spoke in a high, nasal singsong, rather like the recitative of an opera.

We could not understand a word of his singsong nor could our Dutch friends either. He spoke in old Javanese which is quite unlike modern Malay but which the *Orang Javas* can understand well enough. So next day Manisan was able to tell us the plot of the play.

It seems that the singsong man was no less than the King of Heaven himself. His song told how the gods, Brahma, Vishnu, Siva, and others, were being besieged by a wicked giant.

When the giant appeared we didn't recognize him right off because he was actually somewhat smaller than the other actors. But that made no difference. He carried a short, broad sword such as giants always carry if we had only known it. Also, his mask clearly showed that he was not a good giant but a wicked one.

The masks of virtuous characters such as the gods had long, pointed noses, sloping foreheads and receding chins. Their eyes were long and almond-shaped under arched brows. They were the Javanese ideal of beauty

148

as well as virtue. The giant, on the other hand, had a full forehead, bulbous nose, round eyes, and a big, wide-open mouth.

The Hindu giant, like the Greek Achilles, was invulnerable except for one particular spot—the tip of his tongue. His tongue was stuck out, painted black, and tipped with red to show exactly where the crucial spot was.

In spite of the conspicuousness of his vulnerable spot, the giant could not be killed by any of the gods. He could be slain only by a mortal—a pure man, without fear and beyond reproach. A great deal of time was spent in telling about all of this. The small giant stood patiently by, his round eyes popping and his tongue out.

At last the mortal beyond reproach, the Hindu Sir Galahad, appeared. He was Ardjuna who, besides being pure and brave, was also exceedingly good-looking. As he was a mortal, he wore no mask. He had light, olive skin, a rather long nose and a slightly sloping forehead. He was a real life model of the exaggerated masks of good and beautiful people.

Having gotten hold of Ardjuna, the gods had to prove his worth. They sent seven beautiful nymphs to tempt him with their charms. They did this by dancing around decorously while Ardjuna stood with his arms folded, looking virtuous. Having proved himself by resisting the nymphs, Ardjuna was ready now to have a go at the giant.

But this took time, everything took a lot of time. The orchestra played slowly with frequent pauses. The actors moved and paused with it, and intoned their singsong at great length. There were a great many of them because once a character had appeared on the stage, he stayed there although, according to the story, he was actually miles away or even in another country.

Meanwhile the audience chatted and laughed, ate, drank, and smoked. Lemonade and cakes were peddled around and the vendors and their customers made fully as much noise as the actors and the orchestra.

Needless to say, Ardjuna eventually killed the little giant by pricking him with a sword right on his vulnerable red spot. Then the gods rewarded Ardjuna by giving him a kingdom. He also married the nymphs and they—all eight of them—lived happily ever afterward.

By that time it was midnight and we got up from our hard chairs practically paralyzed. The rest of the audience, however, were sorry it had ended so soon. For many *wayang* shows, the good long ones, continue until daybreak.

We had been bored by the length of the play and by having to guess at its story. But walking home among the black and silvery shadows, I felt that I had seen a fairyland—and a real one too—because everyone believed in it.

20

WHEN April came with only showers such as we would have at home, our spirits rose with the lifting clouds. Now that the rainy monsoon was ending we felt that we had been through something or other. Somehow things would change now for the better. Our horizon was clearing not only psychologically but in actuality, because we were soon going to have electric light.

At this time the scene was enlivened too by the appearance of the stupendous, the almost unbelievable Mijnheer Agostino de Vasca. The arrival of De Vasca, just when the power plant had been finished, was not due to coincidence but to design. However, we didn't know that and were tremendously thrilled when Boy One announced that we had an unknown visitor.

We had just finished our siestas and so were able to dress quickly in our best. Mother, agog with curiosity, put on a flowered print. I put on a dress and even wore my shoes. The boys slicked themselves up by putting on shirts and combing their hair.

When Mother entered the living room a tremendously fat man rose from the armchair he overflowed and which partially rose with him. He pushed it off his rump, rushed to Mother, took her hand and covered it with resounding kisses.

Then bowing, he said in a booming voice: "De Vasca!"

Mother had to step back a little to look up at him over his overhanging stomach which was naked in a wide swathe above the tops of his pants. Above the bare swathe was a cotton undershirt with black hairs curling through the mesh. At top and toe he was more nattily attired; he wore black patent-leather pumps but no socks, and a broad-brimmed panama with a red band. His swarthy face was tremendously mustached and a gold ring twinkled in each ear.

"How do you do, Mijnheer De Vasca?" said Mother in a rather faint tone. She was overwhelmed by the sheer quantity of our visitor.

Mijnheer De Vasca wedged himself back into his chair, leaned forward, hands on knees, and stared at Mother. "I could never believe it! Never! I have been told how beautiful American ladies are, but I could never believe it until this moment!"

Mother blushed a little. She thought that she *was* rather pretty but she was not used to such overpowering compliments. She was to become quite inured to them after a short acquaintance with De Vasca.

The gentleman now turned to us and repeated that he never could believe it! He had heard how fine and handsome American children were but had not been able to credit it until now. He complimented Mother on our excellent manners. Our manners, never of the best, were in complete abeyance now. We stood rooted to the spot, staring at our visitor in utter astonishment.

Mijnheer De Vasca explained that he was our neighbor, as he lived only ten miles away. He had intended to call on us long ago but had somehow just now gotten around to it. How he regretted not coming sooner, now that he know how charming and delightful we were and Mother—how beautiful she was! And the worthy Mijnheer Stryker! How De Vasca longed to make his acquaintance!

Mother said she was sorry that Dad was out at work.

"At work!" exclaimed De Vasca. "He works, then, in the afternoon? I have, of course, heard how energetic

Americans are. But I had no idea that they worked in the afternoon!"

Mother assured De Vasca that they frequently did. Then she sent Peter for Boy One to bring tea and also to ask Miss Blue if she would join us. Miss Blue generally did not care to join us and took her tea alone. But today De Vasca's booming voice must have penetrated to her room and curiosity brought her out.

He kissed her hand almost as voraciously as he had Mother's and began to say that he had never been able to believe that American ladies . . . Miss Blue cut him short by coldly informing him that she was British.

De Vasca was slightly deflated for a moment but with the appearance of the tea tray he revived. "Tea!" he exclaimed. How he adored tea! He was almost as fond of tea as he was of . . . well . . . say, gin and bitters.

Catching his delicate allusion, Mother immediately sent Boy One to fetch some. De Vasca mixed his *pijt* and tossed it off, then he prepared another, set it at his elbow and was ready to talk about himself.

He said he was a planter, but did not have a tremendous plantation like Daringo, only a small one. In his small way he was, it happened, also a tapioca planter.

"But," he said, holding up a forefinger like a sausage, "I'm only a teeny, weeny planter."

At this, we children, who were beginning to come out of our trance, started to giggle, and Mother had to glance at us severely. De Vasca smiled and murmured that we had delightful manners. Then he drained his *pijt*, prepared another and went on to say that he did

154

not have a big, modern factory such as he understood Mijnheer Stryker planned to build. As for a power plant—quite beyond his means, although there was nothing he would like to have so much as electricity.

Down went another *pijt* and De Vasca began to tell us about all his family. They were of Portuguese origin, he said, and belonged to the nobility. They had come to Java long ago when the Portuguese were lords of the Indies. Sad times followed when the boorish Hollanders had ousted the glamorous Latins and the De Vasca family fortunes had declined. But pouring another drink, De Vasca brightened and said that his mother was a real Javanese princess. What did we think of that?

We were absolutely fascinated, not so much by De Vasca's mother as by himself. Flattered by our interest, he proceeded to tell us all about her. She had been the wife of a Javanese raja. When the raja died she and the other widows were, as adat ordained, to be burned on their lord's funeral pyre. But at the last moment, just as the match was set to the fagots, De Vasca's father arrived on the scene and snatched the beautiful princess from her dreadful fate.

"Now," boomed De Vasca. "What do you think of that?"

It sounded somehow vaguely familiar to me. I recalled something of the sort in *Around the World in Eighty Days*. But I couldn't bring myself to doubt the persuasive Mijnheer Vasca.

Miss Blue could. She acidly observed that the practice of suttee had been abolished in Java at least a century

155

ago. That being the case, just how old might Mijnheer De Vasca's mother be? De Vasca's swallowed his *pijt* and was putting his mind on some plausible reply when he caught sight of Dad, and with obvious relief he jumped to his feet and rushed to greet him.

"And you've been out in the fields until nearly six o'clock! What energy! What drive! What an extraordinary man you must be, Mijnheer Stryker! I have heard of your plans here and about your power plant also. It is all colossal! Napoleonic!"

"Thank you," said Dad. "Won't you have a drink?"

"I've already had one. Allow me to offer *you* one." De Vasca poured the last of the gin into a glass and handed it to Dad. Dad didn't like his gin straight but he was so overwhelmed by De Vasca that he sat down and drained it off.

"You'll have some more, won't you?" De Vasca asked hospitably. He glanced at the empty bottle and then at Boy One who, having also fallen under the De Vasca spell, obediently went to fetch another.

De Vasca spoke at length and with intense admiration about Dad's activities. He seemed to be particularly interested in the power plant and asked how much electricity it provided. When Dad told him, De Vasca exclaimed that he could never use that much. Dad said he would eventually, when all of his land was producing and the factory was processing a large quantity of tapioca. But that, De Vasca pointed out, would be well in the future. Dad sadly agreed that it *would* be well in the future. Meanwhile, De Vasca asked, why couldn't

Dad sell some of his electricity? De Vasca would like very much to have it on his own plantation.

Dad said he would think it over. Then, glancing at his watch, he saw it was dinnertime. As De Vasca gave no signs of leaving, Dad asked if he wouldn't like to stay. De Vasca replied that he certainly would.

At the table he regaled us with an endless stream of conversation. Apparently forgetting Miss Blue's doubts about the story of his mother, the Javanese princess, he told it again with added details and embellishments. Then he went on to recount many of his own remarkable exploits, daring deeds, and hairbreadth escapes. The boys and I were enthralled and hoped it would go on forever. Our elders, however, when their first amazement had worn off, began to look a little as though they hoped it would *not* go on forever.

But after dinner De Vasca settled himself in his armchair, mixed his *pijt*, and prepared to make an evening of it. Miss Blue, as usual, retired to her room. Though it was not yet bedtime for Frank and Henry, Mother said that it was and took them off. As she left the room she glanced at Dad, and it was an apologetic glance to let him know that she was not coming back. She was leaving him to hold the bag.

Dad sent a look of bitter reproach after Mother. He didn't think he could stand an evening of De Vasca. But Jim, Peter, and I were prepared to thoroughly enjoy a continuation of the tall tales. Unfortunately, they did not continue. De Vasca returned to the subject of electricity. It was dull and we couldn't understand much about it. He was still at it when the boys and I finally went to bed.

Later, I gathered that Dad had been prepared to consider selling De Vasca some electricity. However, in talking it over, he discovered that De Vasca was not in a position to pay for it right away. He would, he told Dad, pay later. But at the present time he didn't even have the money to pay for having the poles and wires carried over to his place. So that also would have to be taken care of in the indefinite future.

Dad said that he was rather hard up himself. He didn't think he could supply electricity under those conditions. De Vasca took his refusal cheerfully, dropped the subject, and returned to his personal exploits. He kept at it until two in the morning. Then he went off with a hearty: "Good evening!" and left Dad absolutely exhausted.

21

THOUGH Mijnheer De Vasca was unable to obtain electricity on the cuff, so to speak, he was invited to our celebration of the great night when lights were first to shine at Daringo. Dad suggested that he come a little early so as to have a drink at our house before going to the dinner party at the inn.

De Vasca accepted the suggestion and came early,

very early indeed. It was only four o'clock when we saw approaching what appeared to be a small cavalry detachment. De Vasca had brought his sons—about fifteen of them.

The boys ranged from youngsters as small as Jim to others who were as tall as their own father. Some, like Mijnheer De Vasca, were fat and some were thin; some were as swarthy as he, others as dark as Javanese. Others again, surprisingly, were very blond.

All of them, fat and thin, dark and fair, sat themselves down on the porch and said they had had a long hard ride and were very thirsty. Mother couldn't decide which of the De Vasca sons were of gin-drinking age. So in addition to the bottle of gin, she had Boy One bring a pitcher of lemonade. But, apparently none of the De Vascas were teetotalers. They all, even the twelve-year-old, mixed *pijts*, drank up, and mixed themselves some more. When the second bottle of gin was opened, De Vasca sternly told some of the younger boys to run along and play now, they had had enough. But he himself and the older ones had not had enough and kept right on with it.

The number and variety of the De Vasca boys was confusing; though they were all introduced we couldn't remember their names. We never did get them straight because on subsequent visits De Vasca brought just as many of them but they were not all the same boys. We couldn't imagine how many sons he must have at home to be able to form a cavalcade without bringing the same ones every time.

On our first meeting with them, the fattest and blondest of the grown-up boys made quite an impression on us. He sat industriously picking his nose while he drank his *pijts*. As the nose picking went on until we were staring in fascination, De Vasca shouted something to the lad in Portuguese. When the nose picking stopped temporarily, De Vasca turned to Mother.

"Charming lad, is he not, Nicodemus? His mother was a lovely creature—a Dutchwoman and he looks just like her."

We couldn't honestly agree that Nicodemus looked like a lovely creature but he was indubitably of Dutch blondness. Could the same fair Dutchwoman have mothered the swarthy sons also? A mingling of strains plays strange tricks, but certainly the same woman couldn't be the mother of all these sons.

Mother was intrigued by the problem and, seeking information, said that she was sorry Mevrouw De Vasca had not come along with the rest of them. De Vasca replied that he never took a wife anywhere. Still intrigued, Mother tried another tack and asked if De Vasca had been married more than once. De Vasca said that he had had many, many wives.

At this, Mother and Miss Blue both leaned forward, all ears to hear just how many and of what sorts. But at that moment Dad arrived and De Vasca turned to him, leaving his mysterious matrimonial alliances up in the air.

After he had invited Dad to sit down and have a drink, De Vasca took up his favorite subject of electricity. He said again that he would like to have it but unfortunately still was unable to pay for it. Dad said, as before, that he really could not undertake to supply electricity without payment.

Again, De Vasca was not disgruntled and rose with cheerful alacrity when it was time to go to the inn for dinner. In regard to dinner, Mother had been doing some fast thinking about her fifteen unexpected guests. She decided that the four oldest of the De Vasca sons would take the place of our own boys at dinner. Our boys and the rest of the De Vascas would have a scratch meal at our house.

At the inn, when we introduced Mijnheer De Vasca and his four big boys to our Dutch friends, they made their usual impression. It was a moment or two before even loquacious Klaut could find his voice.

Finally he remarked that it was nearly dark, time for the ceremonial turning on of the lights. He invited Dad to make a speech for the occasion but as Dad couldn't think of a speech, Klaut made one himself. It was very long and all about the great accomplishment of bringing modern progress to the darkness of Daringo. It was hard for De Vasca to listen to anyone else speak, so as soon as Klaut paused for breath, he took up the theme and added that Dad was really Napoleonic.

By this time it was very dark indeed. Feeling that De Vasca might go on until midnight, Dad strode over and turned the light switch.

After months of lamplight, the room seemed dazzlingly bright. We all looked at each other and blinked.

Impelled by a desire for more brightness, we went all over the inn turning on lights just to see how bright electricity could be.

Looking out, I saw that my brothers had done the same at our house and it was blazing like a beacon too. The other houses were dark because all the servants had gone to the village to make merry in honor of the electric lights. Seeing the village brightly lighted through the trees, Mevrouw Accountant Aken said she was so glad because now it looked so cheerful.

However it looked, the village was not cheerful. It was in a state of panic.

The electric power plant had been built by skilled workers who had been brought in from Batavia. Several of those who remained to operate the plant lived in their own separate quarters nearby and did not mingle with the villagers. So far as the villagers were concerned, the power plant was just a building. The poles which had been set up along the main street and around the square were merely curious objects.

But our old friend Sito, who had been in Wazi, was able to tell everyone about electricity. It could bite people and it *would* bite them if they didn't watch out!

Everyone looked uneasily at the tall poles strung with ropes and each having a large, round glass eye. It was known that the celebration was being held because of something the poles were going to do that very night.

When a blinding light flashed into each glass eye, it was obvious that things were going to happen. The villagers did not wait to see what but turned and fled into the darkness.

Nothing happened. The poles with their blazing eyes remained motionless. Gingerly, some of the Javanese approached them. A daring youth went up and touched a pole with his finger. He turned a triumphant glance on his timid friends. It *didn't* bite, see!

Everyone made sure of it by touching the pole. The next thing for the daring lad to do was to climb the pole and see if the glaring glass eye could bite. He withdrew his hand from the bulb in a hurry. It *did* bite!

No, the lad shouted, it had not bitten him. The eye was merely very hot. Then wrapping his turban around his hand he continued his investigations. He found that he could unscrew the eye but surprisingly the light went out. He threw the bulb down so his friends could examine it. When it broke with a loud bang, everyone laughed heartily.

The lad laughed at his exploit also. There must be something else he could do to amuse the crowd. There was. He put his finger into the little hole where the bulb had been. He fell and broke the shoulder of a man standing beneath him, and he broke his own leg when he hit the ground. He had found out the truth about electricity—it *did* bite!

Later, when telephones were installed in the *Orang Blandas'* houses, the inn, the office building, and the hospital, the little black boxes were cautiously approached and touched but they seemed to be harmless.

But on the evening after his black box had been put on the wall, *Tuan* Aken acted very strangely. Dinner was ready and the Aken's Boy One knew that Doctor Klopper was expected. But *Tuan Obat*, Lord Medicine, was late—probably still at the hospital. *Tuan* Aken went to the black box and removing a long, sticklike part of it, put it to his hear. Then he spoke into the little hole in the box.

Why, the poor *Tuan* had gone crazy! Boy One was too polite to laugh but he could not repress a smile. Aken saw his smile. He beckoned Boy One and put the stick thing to his ear. Willing to humor the poor *Tuan*, Boy One smiled good-naturedly.

Then the spirit spoke, "All right, Aken. Sorry to keep you waiting. I'll be there in ten minutes."

Boy One recoiled in horror. He never went near the black box again even to dust it. News of his frightful experience was spread abroad. No *Orange Javas* would ever approach any of the black boxes. Many took the precaution of leaving the room when the bell rang and the spirit was about to speak.

Ice, too was understood to be produced by that devilish electricity, but it was just harmless blocks of glass. When the first block had been carried to the inn and put in a big box, everyone gathered to make merry-merry in its honor. All of the Europeans were there and dressed in their best. When the block of glass was brought in on a tray, *Tuan* Klaut made a speech. Then he broke pieces off the block. Surprisingly, the pieces were put into the highball glasses. The servants all

164

glanced at each other in astonishment. Wasn't it dangerous to put chips of glass into the drinks?

Everyone raised his glass and said words. Then they did not drink immediately but stood feeling their glasses grow cold in their hands. Cold—ice cold, after all those months of muggy, tepid drinks. It was worth a party!

At last everyone raised his glass to his lips. "Aha—aha—" they said. They drank to the last drop, then put their glasses on the table to be filled with more chips.

The glass chips were not only obviously harmless but very pretty, the servants thought. They put some in a glass jar to take home as curiosities. But by the time the party was over the glass chips had disappeared and in their place was only a little water. There *was* magic in the glass chips, after all!

Now Dad remembered that he was supposed to provide his employees with some form of amusement. He had not had time to think about it before but with the electricity installed, why not have some movie shows. However, recalling the effects of the train, the lights, and the telephone, he went about it cautiously.

After the projector and screen had arrived from Batavia, Dad set them up himself in the market shed. Selecting the *Orang policeys* as the braver portion of the population, he invited them to come to the shed late one night after most people had gone to bed.

The *policeys* were, of course, already holding hands. Telling them to keep hold and not to be scared, Dad switched off the lights and started the film.

He had expected the *policeys* to run but they remained motionless; he had expected them to squeal with terror but they remained silent. Were they paralyzed, struck dumb with fear? Dad didn't want to have the wits scared out of his police force, so he stopped the film and turned on the lights.

They were not, at least, struck dumb because they all began to talk at once. The chief of police, asserting himself, made the others hush so that Dad could hear him. "Had *Tuan Besar* expected them to be frightened at seeing ghosts? Why, they had seen them dozens of times. Everyone saw ghosts and even little children are not afraid of them."

Feeling that Dad was perhaps disappointed at this offhand reaction to his ghosts, the chief of police politely added that he had never seen American ghosts before. They were something quite new. It was a very interesting experience to see them. Now, would *Tuan Besar* please turn off the lights and start his *guna-guna* again so they could see what else the ghosts would do?

The rest of the villagers were no more afraid of ghosts than the *policeys* were. Next night they all came to see the show. The audience was at first silent and solemn as people should be when seeing spirits. However, when one ghost threw a pie at another ghost, they could not help laughing. These American ghosts were highly diverting!

Another performance was demanded on the following evening and Dad obliged again. As more performances were requested, he taught one of the power-plant gang how to run the projector. After that there was a show every night. The shed was always packed with spectators who watched the movie with breathless interest. They shrieked with laughter when pies were thrown and howled in terror when someone was almost hit by a train.

The movies, most potent and insidious of American *guna-guna*, broke the reserve of adat.

22

THE first load of tapioca cuttings went out to the fields headed by a procession. Planting as well as plowing had to be started with a religious ceremony which was, of course, followed by three days of *ramee-ramee*.

The cuttings or canes looked very unpromising, being merely endless rows of leafless sticks. We didn't join Torat in his prayers for the success of the crop. But we were all anxious about it knowing how very, very much depended on it.

"There's a lot of money planted there," said Dad. And a lot of time, he might have added, months of unceasing, back-breaking work.

When the fields had been planted they needed only a little hoeing to keep down the weeds. But it turned out that an armed patrol was required to drive away the monkeys. They had, of course, been greatly interested in the work of clearing, cutting, and uprooting. They were sorry when it ended and decided to carry on themselves. So they came down out of the treetops and proceeded to pull up the newly planted canes. That was the idea, wasn't it? Everyone had been pulling things up. Why not carry on the good work?

Armed men were sent into the fields and after some casualties the monkeys learned to keep out. But the wild boars couldn't learn. They came out of the jungle at night and didn't merely uproot the canes but ate them too. A boar-hunting brigade was organized and put on permanent duty.

Guarded from the hungry boars, the tapioca crop was well started but would not, of course, mature until the following May. Meanwhile, more land, the whole of his ten thousand acres, Dad hoped, would be cleared and ready for planting next year. That would require a good many more workers and finding them did not seem an easy task.

Besides attempting to acquire more labor, Dad had to lay plans for the factory which was to stand at the end of the railroad line where an unloading shed had been built. Its site had been leveled and Dad marked it off with strings but more than that he couldn't do. We were amazed to learn that Dad was unable to build the factory all by himself. An engineer was coming from home to build it, supervise the installation of the machinery, and then he would be put in permanent charge of the whole works.

The engineer, Mr. Westlock, was already on his

168

way and Dad was awaiting his arrival impatiently. He was in a hurry about his factory but also, I think, he was looking forward to the companionship of another American. Someone hard-working, efficient, and thorough like himself, bogged down as he was in this land of slowness, inefficiency, and adat.

Mother was also impatient over the new arrival because Mr. Westlock was married. An American woman was coming to Daringo! Mevrouws Klaut, Aken, and Vos were, of course, very nice, very nice indeed, Mother said, but how she longed to be with an American again. The Westlocks, it seemed, were young and recently married. Mother was thrilled at the thought of the young bride. She anxiously watched the building of the Westlocks' house. She wanted everything to be as nice as possible for the young girl who had never been in the East before.

Mother confused the carpenters who were following Dad's strictly utilitarian plan by suggesting improvements in the bride's house. With many vague gestures she indicated that the dining room must be longer and should have a bay window. A bay window was beyond the carpenters' powers but Mother saw with satisfaction that the dining room was at least long enough this time for a sideboard.

Mother devoted much thought to the Westlocks' furniture and urged the carpenters to do their very best with it. However, their furniture would not be finished by the time the Westlocks arrived so they would have to stay at the inn until their house was ready for them.

Mother was glad that the young Americans would arrive in June when the weather was at its best; dry, but not with the scorching dryness of the later summer months.

But the excellence of the weather entailed another obligation on us. Mijnheer De Vasca and various of his male offspring had been constant callers and he had long been urging a return visit. What we had seen of the De Vascas didn't make us anxious to meet the rest of the family and we had used the rains as an excuse. Now, De Vasca pointed out, we had no such excuse so we simply must come.

Early one Sunday morning we started off on ponies and rode for several miles along the jungle path toward Wazi. Then we turned off the path into what was only a trail which had been opened, apparently, by the De Vasca cavalcade when they had come to see us. We had known that the De Vascas liked us a lot but had not realized that they had had to break through virgin jungle to reach us.

When we had passed beyond the trees and rode through De Vasca's cassava fields, Dad observed them intently. We made no comment but we could see that they were not as well kept as our own. In fact, in many places the weeds had grown higher than the canes.

We saw De Vasca's stomach at the top of his porch steps as soon as we spied his house through the trees. He rushed down to help Mother dismount and to kiss her hand despite her attempts to keep it away from him.

De Vasca shouted to Nicodemus to help me off my horse. But by the time he got there I had got down myself.

De Vasca swept us up onto the porch which was crowded with people of all ages, sizes, and colors. They all stared at us with great curiosity but our host didn't introduce us. He pulled aside a batik door curtain and ushered us into a large, dim room.

In the center of the room was a little old Javanese woman, jewels in her ears and hair and wearing a black silk waist over her silk sarong. She was posed as for a photograph and leaned against a table, supporting her head with two thoughtful fingers. In her other hand was a large handkerchief which she held so that it fell in graceful folds.

"The Princess, my mother," De Vasca boomed.

Dad bowed to her and Mother shook her hand. The old woman said nothing but motioned us, with a wave of her handkerchief, to be seated. Then she resumed her pose and stared before her in silence.

It seemed that someone should say something so De Vasca, of course, began to talk. He spoke first of his gratification at our visit and then, for the umpteenth time, began to tell us his mother's story. Though she gave no indication of hearing him, De Vasca seemed inspired by her presence and told the tale with embellishments we had not heard before. Obviously, it was a story which improved with telling and De Vasca was all wound up like a top.

"Had it not been for my father's daring and bravery,"

he said with tears in his eyes, "my dear and honored mother would have perished in the flames."

Like an automaton came to life, the old woman interrupted in English, "If I had had a choice between the flames and your father, I know what my choice would have been. The life that man led me—"

De Vasca laughed deprecatingly. "She likes her joke. She's very jolly, isn't she?"

We didn't think the Princess was exactly what we would call jolly. And after her single remark she fell silent again. De Vasca couldn't find anything else to say and neither could we. Finally, he rose and remarked, as though the thought had just struck him, that we must meet his wife.

She was among the crowd out on the porch and was obviously not the blond Dutchwoman who was the mother of Nicodemus. Mother was never able to find out what had happened to that lovely creature. This Mevrouw De Vasca was lovely too in her way, a tall, dark woman who had once been extremely beautiful. Her classic features were worn but still noble and imposing. She looked like a mask of the Tragic Muse—until she smiled and spoke, then the classic mask cracked into wrinkles and sheer stupidity showed forth.

She giggled and smirked when we were introduced. Then clapped her hands for a servant who brought a tray with glasses of warm, pink lemonade for the women and girls. De Vasca and his sons, of course, had *pijts* with Dad.

Over his drink, Vasca hissed at his wife. She had forgotten to introduce her daughters to us. There were about eight of them and the youngest, Mevrouw Vasca said, was little Araminta who was ten.

There were a number of other, smaller children who seemed to be unaccounted for. One, a brown five-year-old girl stepped forward, pointed to herself and said in Malay: "Me too!"

Mevrouw De Vasca stopped giggling and hissed at the child angrily. A Javanese woman who had been standing in the background advanced with a child in her arms and said, "Him too!"

De Vasca chuckled. "It's a lonely life on a plantation, Mijnheer Stryker. One must pass the time somehow or other, must one not?"

While Dad was trying to decide whether to answer yes or no, Mother tactfully changed the subject by saying what a beautiful place the De Vascas had.

The place, that is the spot itself, was lovely with trees and flowering vines and flowers. But there was really nothing to praise about it but natural beauty. The house consisted of a great many bamboo lean-tos that sagged rather precariously against the original, central structure. Apparently De Vasca had enlarged his house haphazardly as his family increased and the result was as variegated as the offspring themselves.

Besides being haphazard, the De Vasca homestead was very dirty. Innumerable pink lemonades and *pijts* had been served on the long, rambling porch which looked as though it had never been scrubbed. The family or families themselves seemed rather unscrubbed too, though they all wore gold earrings and wafted strong perfumes.

We remembered the Rawleys and one of their principles that one must *not* let oneself go in the tropics. We had not taken this dictum very seriously until the De Vascas showed us how far one *could* go. The De Vascas, in going, had not gone native because the Javanese were clean, industrious, and sober. We were unacquainted with Portuguese home life but it could never have been like this. It must have been De Vasca himself with his exuberant imagination and vitality, who had literally and figuratively created a world of his own.

Now after the Gargantuan *rijst tafel,* we were offered siestas which we refused through fear of the De Vasca wild life. We sat on the porch propping our eyelids open until our hosts finished their naps. Then the fun began again with more lemonades and *pijts.*

Dad said afterward that he was awash with a nauseous mixture of both, when De Vasca insisted on showing him his tapioca factory. They were outdoors walking around in the hot sun for a long time. When they returned Dad made no comment.

On our way home Dad said the factory was built very much in the same style as the house. As far as he could see, it was run more or less on the lines of Mevrouw De Vasca's housekeeping.

No wonder De Vasca was only a teeny, weeny planter! Dad shuddered to think of the quality of his starch.

23

WHEN we caught sight of the Westlocks on the deck of the boat they looked just as we hoped they would. Tall, thin, and even from a distance, typically American.

It was Sunday so a whole trainload of people had ridden down with us to meet them. Dad had rejected Mijnheer Klaut's suggestion of an official welcome with flowers, flags, and speeches. It would strike the Westlocks as strange and foreign, Dad thought. But as soon as the boat neared the dock we began to wave, and kept waving while it was being tied up.

As soon as the gangplank was lowered, we rushed up to shake hands. Close to, the Westlocks were even more American than at a distance. Both had brownish hair and blueish eyes, and Mrs. Westlock was very pretty. They were dressed practically alike in seersucker suits and brown-and-white saddle shoes. Mr. Westlock was particularly perfect because he wore horn-rimmed glasses.

The Westlocks may have been surprised at the enthusiasm of our greetings but they responded nobly and as though we were all old friends. Mother immediately asked Mrs. Westlock how long she had been married. Only three months! Mother beamed—a bride! And her first name was Helen, Mrs. Westlock said. How nice, said Mother—Helen! We began to call her Helen right away and her husband's name was John.

John was explaining to Dad that their furniture was on the boat. Dad had written that the Westlocks need not bring any with them. But if they wanted to, there was cargo space on a boat from New York. Luckily there had also been space on the boat from Batavia to Daringo. John would see to the unloading himself, he said.

Dad insisted that unloading was Mijnheer Vos's job. John and Helen must come right up to our house and have lunch with us.

Helen was delighted with the jungle, the mighty trees, the vines, and wild orchids. Mother must have her house full of lovely jungle flowers all the time, she said. Mother replied, apologetically, that for some reason or other she had not gotten around to keeping flowers in the house.

Mother gave the Westlocks *rijst tafel* for lunch. To break them in, as she said. After their first hesitant sampling, the Westlocks seemed to like it, or at least said that they did.

After lunch Mother suggested that they might like a nap.

"A nap!" cried Helen. "When there's so much for us to see!" No indeed, she and John would take a good, long walk.

We watched them go out into the torrid heat and hoped they would not be felled by sunstroke on their very first day in Java. As for us, we went to bed and

176

didn't awaken until the train came tooting out of the jungle loaded with the enormous crates containing the Westlocks' furniture.

Shortly afterward, Helen and John got back from their walk, crimson and dripping with perspiration. They admitted it had been pretty hot and were glad to go take baths in our tin tub. After that, Helen began to wonder if any of her crates of furniture had been damaged, so we all went down to the unloading shed to see.

Our interest in the Westlocks was contagious because all of the *Orang Javas* were there, too. The foreman who was in charge of unloading came and squatted in front of Dad. The men could open the crates right away, he said. Dad replied it could wait as this was Sunday, their day off. But, the foreman said, the men *wanted* to open the crates right away.

The *Orang Javas*, having become acquainted through the Strykers with the wondrous land of the *Orang Americas*, were enthralled by everything that came from there. Extraordinary, sometimes terrifying things had arrived, but the *Orang Javas* were curious to see what was in those big crates. So the coolies went to work and soon, on the shed floor stood what looked just like home—a chintz-covered sofa and two big, fat armchairs.

Mother exclaimed at the pretty chintz. She couldn't resist stroking it. Helen explained that it was probably foolish to bring their things, but she just couldn't bear to leave them. Her parents had given her the living-room set for a wedding present.

177

Mother agreed with her that, of course, Helen had to bring them. Then she sat in a chair and said how comfortable it was after those rattan chairs that raised welts on your back. Helen sat on the sofa to show Mother how deep and cosy it was. I plopped down beside Helen and the boys had to try the furniture too. Then Dad took the other armchair and John perched on the arm of the sofa.

There we all sat just as though we had been in our own living room at home. The Javanese crowded about us admiringly. So that was how the *Orange Americas* sat at home! On tremendous fat furniture covered with beautiful shiny, flowered cloth.

A loud voice boomed, "Well, well, well! So this is where you are!" Mijnheer De Vasca pushed his bulk through the crowd. He had come to pay his respects to the Westlocks. He was effusive and, of course, had never before been able to believe how beautiful American ladies were.

He seized Helen's hand and covered it with smacking kisses. She smiled politely but could not help showing her surprise. Mijnheer De Vasca was exotic! We hadn't realized before just how exotic he was until we saw him twirling his moustache and twinkling his gold earrings at Helen Westlock.

The coolies started to open another crate but Dad stopped them. The furniture couldn't be moved until tomorrow, better leave it crated as the shed was open and damp.

Helen and Mother were disappointed and so was everyone else. The foreman squatted and spoke to Helen.

"What is he saying? What does he want?" she exclaimed. "And what is he crouching down for?"

Dad explained that the man was crouching out of respect to her.

"Why, that's ridiculous! It's degrading. Please tell him to get up right away."

Dad said he couldn't do that. It would be rude, not adat. And besides the man was saying that he and his men would move the furniture even though it *was* Sunday.

By this time the coolies, overcome by curiosity, had already opened another of the crates. It contained the cream and gold bedroom set, which was upholstered in pale blue satin. We all exclaimed admiringly. Mijnheer De Vasca groaned in ecstasy and sat down with his rump overflowing one of the little blue chairs. The bedsteads were upholstered in blue also. They were the very latest thing at home, Helen told Mother.

The truck, with the foreman proudly at the wheel, drew up. Everyone scrambled through the packings to find sheets of paper to put on the furniture so it would not get soiled. Mijnheer De Vasca got up and carried his little blue chair into the truck with his own hands.

The truck drove off to Helen and John's house while we watched a dining-room set of mahogany, varnished and shining, brought out of the next crate.

But the best was yet to come. Out of the last crate came a white, gleaming electric stove, a big shining refrigerator, and an electric washer.

We were struck dumb with admiration. The *Orang*

Javas recoiled. Who could tell when one of these shining white objects would begin to whir and do something alarming?

The white objects remained silent and motionless so they crowded close. Mother told our cook that one white box was a stove. Cook lifted her hands and said, *"Ado, ado, ado!"* Mother hastened to assure her she would not have to touch the fearsome thing as it belonged to the Westlocks.

The tall box, said Boy One sagely, must be where *Tuan* Westlock kept his money. Boy One had seen the safe in Aken's office. The tall box was white but to Boy One it looked very much like a safe. We told him it was not for money but for food. "Aha!" said Boy One: "How clever are the *Orang Americas*! No ants or beetles can get into that box!"

The truck returned and the dining-room furniture and some trunks were loaded into it. Dad told the foreman that was the last load because the floor of the Westlocks' kitchen wouldn't bear the weight of their splendid modern equipment.

When John heard that, he said he had been foolish to bring things which couldn't be used in Java. Better pack them all right up again and send them home. Dad agreed with him or, he suggested, John might sell them in Batavia. Such things were coming into use there in some of the bigger houses. If John could sell these heavy modern conveniences he would be saved the terrific expense of sending them back home.

181

Helen lovingly fingered her glistening stove as she gallantly echoed, "Yes, we'd better send them home or sell them."

Dad hated to see a pretty girl near tears if he could do anything about it. And suddenly he realized that he *could* do something about it. "Why didn't I think of it before? We'll just reinforce the kitchen floor," he said. "Easiest thing in the world!"

The modern equipment was left in solitary spendor in the shed. We followed the truck to the house, Jim and Peter fighting over who should carry the electric fan and Frank and Henry battling over the toaster.

Our Dutch friends had not thought it proper to go down to the shed while the Westlocks' things were being unpacked. But they felt it *was* all right to come to the house and their servants came crowding in with them. Everyone admired and exclaimed; then set to work to unpack household linen, the tableware and kitchen utensils. They even helped the Westlocks put away their clothes. Our Boy Two was entranced with Helen's girdle until someone explained to him that the *Nonya* wore it. Then he put it down, blushing in confusion.

Mevrouw Acountant Aken had her servant set up the bed springs and mattresses. She made the beds herself. When she had smoothed the blue silk bedspreads she stood back and admired them. She could almost cry, she said. They were so beautiful!

Mother was pleased she had thought of making the Westlocks' dining room a few feet longer. When the shiny, mahogany table and the silk-seated chairs were in place, the sideboard gleamed entrancingly at the end of the room.

Mother put the silverware in the sideboard and I helped with the linen. Helen had everything, even cocktail napkins and embroidered doilies and there was a box of candles in with the linen. Tall, artistic blue ones. The very latest thing at home, Helen said.

Mother put them in the silver candlesticks on the sideboard and we stepped back to admire the effect. While we looked, the tall, artistic blue candles sagged and bent double in the heat.

24

MOTHER said that Helen must drop in often. Come in the morning, she said. The Mevrouws generally paid their calls in the afternoon. They were awfully nice, of course, very nice indeed. But mother was anxious to see a great deal of Helen.

Helen said that, of course, she would drop in. But she didn't know about how often. Because she would be so busy. There must be so many things for her to do.

Two weeks later she changed her tune. "But there *isn't* anything to do!" she lamented, as she sat over mid-morning coffee. "Not a single, earthly thing! What do people do here, the women, I mean?"

Mother admitted that they really didn't do anything at all.

"But I can't bear to do nothing," said Helen. "I really can't."

She was used to doing things, it seemed. After graduating from Vassar, she had worked for an advertising agency for several years before she got married. She always liked to keep busy. Didn't Mother like to keep busy, too?

Mother said a little doubtfully that well, yes, she did. But recalling her *jala* enterprise, she added that somehow, here at Daringo, doing things just didn't seem to work out very satisfactorily.

"All right then, we'll just have to find something to do," said Helen in her decisive way. "We don't want to get into a slump, do we?"

Mother had been in a slump for months. But she didn't want to admit to Helen that she rather enjoyed it. Helen made her ashamed of slumping and Mother decided that she should stop it.

She put down her detective story, got up off the sofa, and began to bestir herself. She was going to put on one of her flowered prints every afternoon and she urged us to dress a little better, also. Now, in late June, school was over, so she couldn't urge us to work harder at our lessons. But she suggested that there was probably some little task we could find to do each day. Perhaps there was, but we were very careful not to look for it.

Mother stirred up Cook too, and gave a dinner party

for the Westlocks. She planned to have people in for dinner every week or so. Besides that, she felt sure there must be other things she could do in the way of entertaining and keeping busy.

Helen's energy made a great impression on me also. I thought she was wonderful. Besides being so full of pep, she was so pretty and so smart too. I wanted to be just like her. I began to wear dresses instead of sarongs and even to brush my hair. I got out my shoes and even went to the length of whitening them myself despite the protests of our little maid Saritita, who generally did my chores for me.

Besides keeping myself neatly dressed I would, like Helen, go to college. Then after that, I would get a job with an advertising agency, whatever that might be. When I confided my plans to Helen she said they were just fine. But how about my Latin and math? I told her that as Miss Blue didn't know any, of course I didn't either. Helen immediately said that she would tutor me. But as I was fifteen and had not yet started these important subjects, she didn't think I would ever be able to enter Vassar. But, she added consolingly, some other, more lowly sort of college might be willing to take me.

"Now, that's one thing I can do," Helen said to Mother. "Teach Charlotte Latin and math. And, of course, John and I are going to work hard to learn Malay and Dutch. Now, what else is there to do? How about organizing a woman's club?"

Mother said that a woman's club would be just lovely,

but as there were only five women on the plantation . . .

"But the Javanese women," said Helen. "They certainly need a club."

Mother said perhaps they did but what sort of club did they need. Helen didn't know exactly so Mother suggested that they consult the Mevrouws Klaut and Aken and with Miss Blue who was usually so fruitful with suggestions.

When Mother laid Helen's plan before them, they said that a club of Javanese women and *nonyas* had never been heard of before and they didn't know how it would work out.

Mevrouw Klaut said the only sorts of women's clubs she knew of were garden and bridge clubs. Many of the Javanese women worked in the fields so they probably had enough gardening already. Mevrouw Aken said that she would simply adore to belong to a bridge club, only she didn't know how to play bridge. Miss Blue thought that a tennis club would be best. There was one in North Borneo and she had been its star player.

Helen said that bridge, tennis, and garden clubs were only a waste of time. What she had in mind was a social-service club of some sort. Everyone said that a social-service club sounded awfully nice and they would just love to belong to one. However, no suggestions about the club seemed to be forthcoming. The discussion ended with Mevrouw Aken repeating her enthusiasm for a bridge club.

She brought up bridge again the next time she came to tea. So Mother got out a pack of cards to give her an idea of the game. As soon as Mevrouw Aken had gotten the idea, Mother, Helen, and Mevrouw Klaut sat down to play a hand and show her how it went. Mevrouw Aken caught on quickly and just as she had predicted, she simply adored it. The others, now they had begun to play, remembered that they were fond of bridge also and soon they were at it every afternoon. That was the beginning and the end of the Daringo Women's Social-Service Club.

But bridge was only something to kill time, Helen still insisted, and she had something more important to do. She was going to organize her housekeeping on really up-to-date and efficient lines, now that she had her new kitchen—her *completely* new kitchen. It had *not* proved the easiest thing in the world to reinforce the floor of the former one. In fact, the new kitchen with its solid cement floor had taken a month to build.

When we saw the refrigerator, the stove, and the washer standing monumentally on the solid cement floor, we all agreed that the new kitchen was well worth while. Everyone was pleased with it except Helen's cook, who stood in the doorway biting her nails. She wouldn't dare to tamper with the tricky electrical spirits. She wouldn't go near them for love or higher wages.

Mother tried to embolden her by turning the switches of the stove to show her how easy it was. And she explained that there was nothing that had to be done to the refrigerator except to defrost it once a week. As to the washer, that was the washwoman's job. But no, nothing would induce the cook to play with spirits.

A Chinese named Gee volunteered to try his hand at it. He had once been cook in a restaurant in Singapore. True, he had had no experience with electrical equipment, but at least he wasn't afraid of it.

Gee was not only daring, he even knew a little English. To show his acquaintance with the white man's world he wore a felt hat. He said his Massa, the Singapore restaurateur, had taught him to wear a hat and to speak English. His Massa had apparently taught him the hard way, for though Gee could understand English fairly well, one of the few phrases he could actually say was: "Massa, please don't beat me!"

Gee soon mastered the magic of the stove. As Mother had remarked, the operation of the refrigerator was even simpler but Gee refused to keep anything in it but his felt hat. Helen made him take his hat out of it because as soon as she had gotten her housekeeping really well organized, she was going to have lots of food to put in her refrigerator.

Our Daringo rice diet horrified Helen. According to what she had learned in a home economics course, it would inevitably result in scurvy, beri-beri, and goodness only knew what else. She was going to find some way of getting fresh meat, milk, butter, and more fruit and vegetables.

Meanwhile, Gee went regularly to the market and brought back a live chicken or fish in a pail. He bought a very meager supply of fruit and vegetables and put them in the cupboard with his felt hat. Then he dished up *rijst tafel* for breakfast, lunch, and dinner. Helen and John finally got used to it and Helen even came to be grateful to Gee for cooking a fresh batch for dinner instead of serving what had been left over from lunch.

Helen made a point of keeping her can of condensed milk in the refrigerator where she also kept bottles of water. The cold water, not iced but just cold, was wonderful. Everyone kept dropping in at the Westlocks' to have a drink of their good, cold water.

Finally, Helen and John got tired of so many thirsty visitors and had their refrigerator moved over to the inn which was a more central location. Dad said it would be the easiest thing in the world to build a little brick base under it!

As neither Gee nor Woman Wash would touch the electric washer, Helen did her laundry herself—for a while. But then, what was the point in doing it herself just to use the washer? So Helen turned the wash over to the washwoman who took it down to the river and beat it clean with a stick.

Though Gee was uncooperative about the washer and the refrigerator, there was one thing he was really good at, the Westlocks boasted. His coffee was simply marvelous! Then Helen discovered that he made it by tying the coffee in a sock which he put into a pan of boiling water. She got John to speak to him severely about that.

"Don't beat me, Massa," said Gee. "I never use a clean sock—allays a dirty one!"

25

THE Westlocks, still fresh and vigorous from a cool climate, brought new life to Daringo during those hot summer months. In addition to Mother's dinner parties which for a while at least, took place every week, other people began to entertain. Apart from their parties and bridge, the women were busy supervising their Women Sews, who were making copies of some of Helen's smart, new clothes. Soon the Mevrouws, Mother, and I blossomed out in more or less successful versions of the latest styles. Miss Blue, needless to say, did not care for them and continued to ruffle around in her rufflies.

Not only was our social life enlivened but our intellects as well. The Westlocks devoted most of their spare time to some serious pursuit or other.

I had lessons with Helen two afternoons a week. I liked Latin and was at first equally enthusiastic about algebra and geometry, although then I couldn't tell them apart. But as time passed and I learned to tell which was which but got no further than that, I became discouraged. I was afraid I would never be able to go to collage but would just have to get married instead.

Helen and John spent several evenings a week studying Malay in an enormous, learned-looked tome they had brought out with them. Their other evenings were to be devoted to the study of Dutch. Mevrouws Klaut and Aken were both anxious to give them lessons. But neither of them would yield the role of teacher to the other. So both ladies spent many evening with the Westlocks, each talking at once, as fast as she could and at the top of her voice.

While John had been working on his detailed scale drawings of the factory, he had felt fresh enough in the evening to devote himself to his studies. But when he had gotten it all down on paper and went out to work laying the cement foundations, he was so tired at night that he really couldn't concentrate.

It was Mevrouw Aken who suggested that instead of having formal lessons, they just play bridge. She and Mevrouw Klaut would teach the Westlocks conversational Dutch as they went along. They remembered to do so a little at first but it was hardly enough for conversational purposes. The Westlocks learned the Dutch for diamonds, hearts, spades, and clubs and how to count to thirteen but that was as far as they got.

Helen kept on studying her learned tome for quite a while. Then she discovered that the Malay in it was so extremely learned that it bore practically no resemblance to the language as ordinarily spoken. She decided she could learn colloquial Malay just as well by merely chatting with her servants.

In spite of having found an easy way to learn Malay and having given up Dutch in favor of bridge, Helen finally grew tired of intellectual pursuits and felt that she must have something much more active to do. There were plenty of ponies on the place but nowhere to ride except through the uninteresting tapioca fields because no one could ride alone in the jungle. I asked Helen to join us children in the river but she was afraid of diseases even if we weren't. So that was no good either.

Dad felt he should do something to provide Helen and the rest of the grownups also with some sort of exercise. Since he and John were up to their necks in cement anyway, it proved easy enough to build a concrete tennis court near the inn. But a net, balls, marker, and rackets had to be ordered from Batavia.

As soon as the equipment arrived, everyone began to play like mad. The men in the early morning and after work as well—if they were not too tired. The women, apart from Mother who was not the athletic type, played at all hours except siesta time when it really was too hot.

On Sundays, Dad took Jim and me in hand. Jim learned quickly but I seemed to have inherited Mother's ineptitude for games. Dad was an excellent player as were Helen and John. But there was no one else in their class and they couldn't make up a decent foursome until Miss Blue swooshed out onto the court. With her skirts lifted a ladylike three inches from the ground, she played a good, fast game.

Miss Blue often referred to the North Borneo tennis club of which, she repeated, she had been the star. She spoke nostalgically of the perfectly wonderful tennis parties Mrs. Tootler-Murfin used to give and suggested that Mother should give some also. Mother's urge to entertain was beginning to subside so she suggested that Miss Blue might like to take charge of the tennis parties.

Miss Blue was glad to do so and arranged them along British colonial lines with a tea table under the trees near the court where everyone sat and sipped as they watched the games.

The De Vascas had been invited to only the first party but they turned up regularly every afternoon. Mijnheer De Vasca, intimidated by Miss Blue, conformed to British customs and drank tea instead of gin. He was too heavy to play, but his sons did, first removing their patent-leather pumps so they could get around quicker in their bare feet.

While we watched the game, monkeys in the treetops watched also, turning their heads to follow the balls just as we did. Real fans, they came to sit on the wire fence around the court. Then they began to run after the balls. First they would bite one, find it inedible and throw it down. Then, deciding that it was an interesting memento anyway, they would carry it into the treetops.

"You should shoot them, Mijnheer Stryker," De Vasca would say.

Dad had not minded shooting the monkeys out in the tapioca fields. But he felt he knew these particular monkeys too well. Shooting them would be like shooting old friends. So the monkeys continued to take the balls home to play with.

"So kind-hearted is Mijnheer Stryker!" De Vasca would murmur. "But whatever you do, *don't* give the monkeys anything to eat!"

Despite his warning, we began to throw crackers and bits of sandwiches to the monkeys. At first they were timid about coming near us but soon grew bolder and came quite close to wait for tidbits.

One afternoon they didn't wait for us. When we got to the court we found them already at the tea table. One sat in an armchair drinking out of the milk pitcher. Another was politely passing the sugar bowl to his friends who sat in the other chairs eating sandwiches.

After that, one of the servants stood on guard at the tea table until we came out and sat in the chair ourselves. Then the monkeys sat on the ground behind us making the gestures of eating. We wouldn't have been at all surprised to hear one say, "Another cucumber sandwich, Mevrouw?"

We got a lot of fun out of tennis and the monkeys did too. It was Helen who suggested that others might enjoy it also. The servants never got any exercise. Tennis would do them good and they were sure to just love it.

When Helen asked them, they said that it *might* do them good and *maybe* they would love it. Gee said he wouldn't mind trying if Missy really wanted him to. The Klauts' Boy One said he would be deeply honored if *Nonya Besar* Westlock would teach him the game. But none of the others seemed to want to try it except our maid, Saritita.

Helen gave them lessons during the early afternoon

194

when no one else wanted the court. Playing in the broiling sun really was something to do, she said. She was very glad to find that another *Orang Java* was really interested in tennis. After she had coached him a while, he began to play with the rest and Helen could take a siesta.

Young Budup was a boar hunter and did his hunting at night. So in the afternoons he was at leisure and could devote himself to tennis. We had noticed him because he spent a good deal of time sitting around our kampong. Obviously he was interested in Saritita.

Budup was strong and agile, he played with a will and soon showed improvement. The others did not and after Helen stopped playing with them herself, they became very slack. They went after the ball languidly or just stood and let it fly past them.

Finally Gee came to Helen, "Don't beat me, Missy! But do we *have* to go out and hit those balls every afternoon? With all the other work we have to do, it's just too much for us!"

Helen said of course they didn't have to play, she thought they enjoyed it. But it seemed that they had only been willing to play because Helen had been so eager to teach them. Saritita and Budup, however, continued to frequent the court. Helen was glad to see that they, at least, didn't hate tennis.

But Gee regretfully disillusioned her about them too. "They are in love, Missy. Even the game of tennis is fun when one is in love!"

26

AFTER some weeks of playing tennis, Budup, who generally lingered out in the road in the evening, came boldly up to our house. He was all dressed up and had let down his sarong so that it fell in dignified folds to his ankles. He wore an undershirt that was obviously new and bought for the occasion, and in a fold of his headcloth was a fresh magnolia. He squatted at the foot of the porch steps and looked up at Dad. It was not adat to call the attention of *Tuan Besar* to one's humble self.

When Dad asked what he wanted, Budup said he had come to ask for Saritita's hand in marriage. Besides being a magistrate, Dad also seemed to be a sort of general father confessor and was consulted by his employees in regard to their private affairs. He did not care for the role at all, so whenever he was consulted on such matters, he always replied: "Do whatever you like."

"But," Mother said, "shouldn't Budup ask Saritita's parents about marrying her?"

Dad said that if Budup hadn't consulted Saritita's parents, it was none of his business. But Mother said that Saritita was only a child and she felt responsible for her.

She asked Saritita if her parents knew that she was going to be married. Saritita replied that they lived so far away that they had not been informed, but her aunt and uncle who had brought her to Daringo had given their permission for her to marry Budup.

When the aunt and uncle heard about Mother's inquiries, they came to see her. The aunt said Saritita's parents would be glad to have her married as she was nearly fifteen and well on the way to being an old maid. The uncle earnestly but unconvincingly assured Mother that the forty guilders which Budup was paying for his bride would be sent off to Saritita's father.

Nevertheless mother was satisfied, and when Saritita shyly told her how much she loved the dashing Budup, Mother was touched. She gave Saritita a present of money and invited her to be married at our house if she wished. Saritita and Budup were delighted with the suggestion and the preparations began.

Budup had a great deal to do. First he had to get his teeth filed short and blackened so that he would not look like a dog and frighten his little bride. Then he went to sit at the feet of the Mohammedan priest who taught him to repeat by heart the words of the marriage ceremony. Mother asked Saritita if she did not need to learn the words also, but Saritita said she would know what to say when the time came.

Saritita prepared by fasting. It was adat, Manisan explained, for a girl to fast before her marriage. She should have only a spoonful of rice and a cup of water a day until she was so thin that a candle could shine through her. Saritita fasted faithfully but she had become plumper of late, and fasting didn't seem to thin her very much.

On the wedding day, Saritita's aunt and several other women came to dress the bride in a new sarong that was tightly wrapped around her torso. Her face was whitened with rice powder and flowers were put in her hair. As a finishing touch, artificial curls were painted on her forehead.

The wedding was to take place in the living room and the marirage feast was to be held on the porch. All of Saritita's and Budup's friends had come to prepare the feast. When all was in readiness, the men went to sit on the porch while the women sat with Saritita in the living room.

We had understood that the wedding was to take place at ten o'clock. But at eleven Budup had not yet appeared. Mother was afraid he would not come at all and that poor Saritita would be jilted at the last moment.

We were all relieved to hear the sound of drums and gongs approaching from the village. The procession was headed by two papier-mâché giants with men under them. Then came Budup himself on a hobbyhorse of papier-mâché, fastened to his shoulders with straps. He held the bridle proudly and pranced along on his own two legs. Several of his friends, also prancing on hobbyhorses, followed him.

The Mohammedan priest walked behind them with dignity. But Torat, the magician, pranced along blithely beating on a tambourine. He was followed by a band, and last came women carrying flowers and paper birds held high on sticks.

Saritita went down the path to meet them. Budup took off his hobbyhorse and laid it on the ground. He took Saritita's hand and then looked around him in confusion, for apparently there was a hitch in the proceedings. After a great deal of running around and whispering, Dad discovered that he was the hitch. He should have gone out to meet Budup who wanted to make a speech.

Budup said he was grateful that Dad had lent his house for the occasion. Then glancing fondly at Saritita, he said: "Now that we are married, I want to tell you that when our first child is born—and it may be quite soon—we will name the child Stryker in honor of *Tuan Besar*."

"Now that you are married!" Dad exclaimed.

"Yes," said Budup, "I was married at the mosque."

The hour's delay was explained. Budup was not tardy. He had been getting married all by himself. *Tuan* Allah teaches that women are inferior beings. Besides having no souls, they are not even worthy of attending their own weddings.

Budup led Saritita into the house where she knelt and washed his feet to show that she herself fully realized that she was inferior. Then Budup led her to the center of the room, where Saritita knelt down and held out a handkerchief into which Budup dropped a few coins to show that he would support her. Then he knelt beside her and put three spoonfuls of rice into her mouth to prove that he would feed her also. But he finished off all the rice remaining in the dish himself.

After that everyone went out to the porch where the feast was laid. The bride and groom did not partake of it but remained side by side in the living room, Saritita looking very pretty and very hungry.

It was the magician Torat who buried the magic boar's head which was a most important feature of a marriage feast. On the snout of the magic boar he placed a gold coin which would bring luck to the newly married pair.

After the feast, another procession was formed to lead Saritita to her new home. Here, it was not her husband but her father-in-law who carried her across the threshold. Then Saritita went and knelt in obeisance at the feet of her mother-in-law.

Everyone agreed that Saritita's wedding and feast had been splendid. A fine meal with lots of food, numerous guests, and a golden coin on the boar's sacred snout augured well for the happiness of the newlyweds.

27

ONE morning a few days later, Dad noticed that the ground where the boar's head was buried had been disturbed. Doubtless, someone had come during the night and dug up the gold coin. Perfectly natural, Dad thought, as so many people knew where it had been buried. To make certain, he asked Boy Two to uncover the head. Boy Two crouched down and said he couldn't do that. It was sacrilege to even touch the sacred boar's head. If anyone had dared to steal the coin— Why, it was unheard of—too frightful for belief!

Dad got out the spade himself and, just as he had thought, the coin was gone. When he mentioned the matter to Mijnheer Klaut, Dad added there was no point in trying to catch the thief. It would probably be impossible for one thing. For another, if gold coins were buried around about, someone was sure to dig them up.

Klaut didn't agree with him. The thief must be sought for and, if possible, found and punished. He insisted, just as Boy Two had done, that stealing the magic coin was a dreadful sacrilege. The *Orang Blandas* must respect the Javanese beliefs. Stealing the coin was a very serious crime.

When it was put to him in this way, Dad heartily agreed with Klaut. So the *policeys* were set to search for the thief. Like all of the Javanese, they were horrified at the theft and they did their best. But the thief could not be found.

Saritita and Budup were in despair about the stealing of their marriage coin. What misfortune could be in store for those whose medding feast had been followed by such a heinous offense? When poor Saritia died at the birth of her son, Stryker, which, incidentally, occurred only five months later, everyone knew it was because the sacred boar had been outraged.

But even though the *policeys* had failed, Torat did not give up the search. Manisan told me he had urged Saritita and Budup not to despair. He, Torat the magician, would find the thief and by his own sure means. And none of the *Orang Blandas* must know anything about it.

Saritita had asked Manisan not to tell anyone. Manisan asked me not to tell anyone. Unfortunately, I kept the secret. And a few days later, when Manisan told me that Torat had found the thief, a coolie named Amat, I didn't tell anyone about that either.

A week later, Doctor Klopper came to dinner with us. After dinner he hinted that he wanted a few words alone with Dad. The Dutch are a little like the Mohammedans in thinking that females should not be told anything important.

After the doctor left, Dad informed us that a man named Amat had been brought to the hospital. Klopper was not absolutely certain about it, but he was pretty sure that Amat had been poisoned.

When Amat died next day, of course we all heard about it. Then I told Dad what I had learned from Manisan. He didn't question her about it because he knew she would deny the whole thing.

That night Dad arranged to have everyone but me go to the movies. I sat in the living room and called Manisan in for a chat. Dad, Mijnheer Klaut, and the chief of police stood close to the window on the dark porch.

Dad had told me to proceed cautiously so at first I talked of trivialities. Then I remarked that it was a shame the thief had not been found.

"Oh, but I told you he had been found," said Manisan. "Don't you remember, *Nonee,* Torat discovered him, a coolie named Amat . . ." Manisan paused. She was not very bright but she could put two and two together. She grew very thoughtful, then went on. "But it was not the Amat who died in the hospital today. Oh, no, it was entirely different Amat!"

I had to be careful. Manisan was not smart but adat taught her that *Orang Javas'* secrets should not be revealed.

"You said you never saw the Amat who stole the coin?" I asked.

"I didn't tell you that, *Nonee.* But as a matter of fact, I never did see him."

"Then how do you know he wasn't the man who was poisoned?" I thought the question didn't prove much one way or the other. But poor Manisan was astonished at my powers of deduction.

She drew close and spoke low. "Listen, if that Amat was the man who stole the coin, I mustn't know it and I mustn't tell it. And you, *Nonee,* mustn't know it and you must never, never tell it. It's *guna-guna,* all this, and dreadful things happen to people who tell about *guna-guna.*"

"That's enough," announced Dad from the porch. When he and the other two men hurried into the room, Manisan cowered in terror, then got up and scuttled away with her teeth chattering. Mijnheer Klaut told the chief of police to go home but Dad said they needed the man to sign the report they were going to write.

"But we had better, much better, not write a report," said Klaut.

"Well," said Dad, "I don't know how far what we heard Manisan say will go toward pinning the guilt on Torat. But that's not our business. Amad died of poison and the information we have must be sent to the police at Wazi."

"But they would much, much rather not have the information," said Klaut. "You see, the authorities prefer to let the Javanese deal with such matters in their own way. To them, stealing a sacred coin should be punished by death. So they think Torat did not commit a crime but administered justice. The authorities would prefer to let it go at that. If you put the information before them, they will be forced to act on it. Don't send in a report, Mijnheer Stryker."

Dad listened thoughtfully. Klaut mistook his silence for assent and went on. "We'll just forget about the whole thing. And you, Charlotte, will not say a word about it, will you?"

Like Dad, I was thoughtful. Could I agree to keep silent about a murder?

Dad answered for me. "Of course not! I'm going to write the report. And you, Mijnheer Klaut, will sign it and the chief of police also."

"Since you insist, I'll sign it," said Klaut. "But in a matter of *guna-guna*, it's far better not to meddle. No one knows what it might lead to—"

"I don't care what it leads to," said Dad. "I have an *adat* too. I won't hush up a cold-blooded murder. *Guna-guna* isn't going to keep me from doing what I consider my duty."

Dad did his duty—to the bitter end. The report was sent, the authorities took action, and further evidence was found against Torat. He was tried and condemned to death at Wazi.

Then, with a Chinese executioner and two Dutch officials, he was brought back to the scene of his crime.

With his hands tied behind his back, he knelt in the center of the public square at Daringo. But no *Orang Javas* were present. They were not willing to witness the death of the powerful sorcerer. Who knew what might come of it?

28

I SHOULD be able to make a good story of this and say that after Dad had turned Torat over to the executioner, *guna-guna* went into operation and dreadful things began to happen. Dad and perhaps Manisan and I also should have broken out in spots and curled up and died.

Manisan *did* expect dreadful things to happen. She went as far toward curling up and dying as autosuggestion could take her. Dad tried to talk her out of it. He talked sensibly but Manisan only replied: "Ado!" Then Dad decided to talk nonsense. He told her that the *Orang Americas* could make *guna-guna also*. Look at their electricity that bit and their black boxes that talked! They were the work of the great American magician, Edison. Dad was a pretty good magician himself, he said. He would use his esoteric powers to ward off *guna-guna* and keep Manisan from harm.

Manisan cheered up considerably. She said that if Dad would give her a powerful American talisman, she would feel quite safe. Dad promised her a talisman, but thinking it over, he wondered what it could be.

His problem was solved by the arrival of a package from home. Dad's mother had sent him a gold-plated razor for his birthday. A modern safety razor was rare in Java. The Dutch used the old-fashioned, straight kind and the Javanese rarely had beards. And this remarkable razor was apparently of solid gold! Manisan was delighted with it. She wore it around her neck on a string and declared that she would never part with it.

In one way or another almost everyone seemed to believe in *guna-guna*. Mijnheer Klaut said it was probably just suggestion but he did know personally of a case. Then he told the old story that everyone in the Far East tells as having happened to a friend of his. The friend, it seems, was a young *Orang Blanda* who had a native mistress. When he abandoned her to marry a white woman, his mistress warned him that she would put a curse on him. But the young man just laughed and went his way. But, the story ends, within six months he was dead of some mysterious and very unpleasant disease.

Mijnheer De Vasca believed in magic implicitly. He added several blood-curdling stories to that of Klaut. The best of them concerned a sacred waringin tree. It stood in the yard of a Dutch family and just on the spot where they wanted to make a tennis court. Of course they knew a sacred tree should not be cut down but they went ahead and did it anyway.

Then dreadful things began to happen. Stones came flying through their windows. And although they rushed right out to look, of course, not a living soul was to be seen. When they took their *bad* they would be suddenly spat upon by an invisible spitter. They would open a bureau drawer and find it full of newborn kittens. Sometimes, when they got into bed at night, they would find it spattered with fresh blood. And so the curse went on and on until they were all dead or in the insane asylum. Mijnheer De Vasca *did* hope that nothing like that would happen to us.

Dad said, "Rot!" in such a tone that De Vasca didn't bring the matter up again—to him. But De Vasca went on about it to Mother and me. Mother said, "Pooh!" and I, with less conviction, echoed her. Despite our poohs, De Vasca told us how *guna-guna* curses could be warded off.

He said his old mother was something of a sorceress herself. She could make magic (guaranteed to be strictly white and harmless) that would keep off evil influences. If Mijnheer Stryker were not so completely skeptical, the Princess would be able to do him a lot of good. But in the face of total disbelief, she could accomplish nothing. But Charlotte here, was more impressionable. The Princess's charms and exorcisms would certainly help me a lot. Mother said, "Pooh!" again but I didn't say anything. I wondered.

De Vasca told us his mother would be glad to come over and try a charm or two. She was, he added, very anxious to come and see us anyway. In that case, Mother said to please ask her to come. But just for a social call as a neighbor and not as a sorceress.

Mother had already invited the De Vasca ladies to call on us. So we couldn't imagine why, if the Princess wanted to visit us, she didn't just come. Why bring up this business about magic? But by this time we had learned that De Vasca was nothing if not devious.

The Princess arrived in a litter borne by four coolies who brought her right up to the porch steps so that her feet would not have to touch the ground. Her head and face were muffled in a silk slendang which she took off only when she sat down in the living room.

Mother said she was delighted to see her again. She added politely but firmly that she was not interested in *guna-guna* and charms. The Princess seemed much more lively than when we had last seen her. She crinkled up her little wizened face and laughed gaily. "Oh, no. No magic! That's all nonsense. We won't speak of magic, but as to charms—"

We expected her to say something else but she only looked at me. She crinkled again and her betel-stained mouth puckered into a rather forced smile. Her tone too was somewhat forced as she said, "Such a lovely young maiden!"

I said, "Thank you."

The Princess uncrinkled and, apparently, changed the subject. She began to talk about her family. She didn't go so far as to say that she was of royal birth but she came of an ancient, aristocratic Javanese family. The De Vascas were a fine family too. Didn't Mother think that the Princess's grandsons were splendid young fellows?

Simply splendid, Mother echoed politely. The Princess went on to say that Nicodemus was a particularly handsome, attractive young man. Why, one would take him for a pure-blooded Dutchman or even an American! Mother, still thinking the Princess had gotten off the subject of me, agreed with that also.

Then the Princess asked if Mother knew the way in which marriages were arranged, not between the young people themselves but between their families. Mother said she had read about such things but really didn't know much about them.

The Princess proceeded to tell her. The two families must be of the same social standing, and should like each other and be congenial. It was best if they lived near each other so that the bride's family would not lose their child entirely. Then there was the question of money. Of course, the bride should have a dowry. Not a great deal, perhaps, but enough so that her husband would not have to support her.

"Then . . ." the Princess closed her eyes and spoke very softly. "The young people should be attracted to each other, should they not?"

I said, vaguely: "I suppose so."

The Princess crowed with delight and beamed at me expectantly. I didn't know what she expected me to say. Also, there was something about her expression that made me uncomfortable so I said nothing. But the Princess redoubled her beams and said: "Then I understand that you would like to marry my grandson Nicodemus!"

I stared at her with my mouth open. Mother's mouth

dropped open too but she found words sooner than I did. "No, Princess, you are quite mistaken. We didn't even know what you were talking about."

"Didn't know what I was talking about!" shrilled the Princess. "Why, I made myself perfectly clear. Nicodemus needs a wife. Your daughter is a little on the skinny side but she'll fill out in time. And your husband could perfectly well afford to give her a dowry."

Mother repeated that the Princess was greatly mistaken. I would not marry for years yet and when I did it would not be Nicodemus.

The Princess crinkled in anger and looked very unpleasant indeed. She said that we should have known that an old woman didn't come all the way through the jungle just for a chat but for some serious purpose.

After the Princess had left, Mother began to laugh. I laughed too but I was upset at the idea of that horrible Nicodemus. I made Mother promise not to breathe it to a soul.

But she did breathe it and to several souls. First Dad said something about wanting to give the whole De Vasca family a kick in the pants. Then both Helen and John began to laugh at me about it. But Manisan took it seriously. After all, she said, here I was pushing sixteen and no husband in sight. So perhaps I should take Nicodemus, fat and unattractive as he was.

Finally, it trickled through to the boys and they went around shouting, "Ya-ya-ya, Nicodemus! Ya-ya-ya, Nicodemus! Nicodemus!"

29

ONE afternoon at two o'clock, purple clouds rolled overhead. The fiery sun disappeared and rain began to fall. During the long, dry summer months we had almost forgotten about rain. Though it did not lower the temperature, its mere wetness was wonderful.

But rain was not wonderful to Dad. It was disastrous. All during the summer he had tried to get more workers but he had not been successful. Working conditions and wages at Daringo were good but somehow the Javanese preferred to stay in their own villages and, as Dad put it, putter around in their own rice fields. They're just crazy, John said. They would rather stay at home than go elsewhere and earn more money.

Now, with the rains starting, what workers Dad had would be bogged down as they had been the previous winter. And by next spring without an increased labor supply, only another twenty-five hundred acres would be cleared and ready for planting. John cheerfully suggested that rain wouldn't interfere with the work. Dad replied that John had not yet seen real rain.

Rain, mud, and adat—how they had played havoc with Dad's plans! He had expected to be able to acquire a plantation within a month and to be sending tapioca back to Roselawn within a year. But his first tapioca crop would not be ripe and ready for processing until next spring, two years after our arrival in Java. It was moving slowly, very slowly and taking time, an awful lot of time.

That being the case, it might occur to some people to abandon the venture entirely. In fact, some of the directors of the Roselawn Glue Company were beginning to think about it. But not Dad. Dad never gave up. He would finish what he had started despite rain, mud, hell, and high water. He would carry on although he would have to use his own salary and his savings also to do so.

John suggested that Dad borrow money instead of putting his shirt into it. But Dad never had borrowed money. And he said he would spend every cent he had in the world rather than do so now.

When all of this seeped through to us, Jim and I were very much concerned. We wondered if it would end in our having to go to the poorhouse. The poorhouse seemed a dreary prospect. Jim had a much better plan in case worse came to worse. We would all put off from Daringo in a small boat and find an uninhabited island where we could live like the Swiss Family Robinson. I agreed that an island would be better than the poorhouse though the idea did not greatly attract me. But Jim said he would like it a lot. I suspected him of hoping for the worst so that his plan could be put into effect.

Mother's reaction to the situation was to suggest firing some or all of the servants. But as the entire domestic staff cost less than seventy-five dollars a month

Dad said that economy would not make much difference. We were living very cheaply at Daringo, anyway.

Jim and I suggested that Miss Blue could go and that she never would be missed. But Dad said that having Miss Blue was the least expensive way to provide for our education. And in regard to our education, Dad went on, Miss Blue wouldn't be teaching Jim and me next year. Now that we would be in Java so much longer than he had expected, Dad planned to send us home next summer. We would live with grandmother in Roselawn and go to high school so that we could be prepared for college.

I said I had decided I didn't want to go to college— that had been only a passing fancy. Jim said he didn't plan to go to college either. He would just stay at Daringo and help Dad with the work. Or if things came to the worst, there was his island scheme which he thought would be best of all. Probably he could catch a lot of wild animals there and sell them to the circus for a whole lot of money. Dad and Mother made no comment on the island and animal scheme but they exchanged a look which meant, next summer off they go to Grandmother.

By the time the afternoon showers had turned to a steady downpour, the factory had been built and the machinery was being installed. The little train brought up all sorts of machines for cutting, grinding, and pulverizing tapioca. We watched them being unloaded and they looked very impressive. Dad watched too, and thought about how much they cost and how long it would be before he had enough tapioca to use them to full capacity.

John worked desperately getting the machinery installed by the coolies whom he had to teach and train as they went along. The rain didn't interfere with his work but John now agreed that the Java rains were really terrific. The weather was just crazy, he said, and did something to him. It was much harder to work efficiently in this crazy place than it was at home.

Helen said, now that the weather was so bad, one must make a special effort not to get into a slump. But despite Vassar, advertising agency, vim and vigor, she slumped in the rain just as everyone else did. And she slumped and lolled around in a sarong, too. At first she said sarongs were sloppy and that going without pants made her feel indecent. But she soon found that being pantless, as well as shoeless and stockingless, was cool.

Helen and I had long since abandoned our mathematical studies as hopeless. As to Latin, Helen said I could get along with it just as well if I studied by myself. Perhaps I could have if I had tried, but detective stories were so much more interesting than the Gallic War. Helen thought so too and spent most of her time on the sofa reading them.

But shortly after New Year's, she was literally forced to get up. Long ago, when the rains began, the pretty chintz slipcover had rotted, spotted, and been thrown away. The blue velvet upholstery had been very hot to sit on until it became thoroughly damp and stayed that way. Then holes appeared in the sofa and in the big armchairs also. Helen thought they were made by the insects that flew around the house or by the invading armies of ants and beetles.

But one evening she found out what caused the holes. A long, pale worm ate his way out of the sofa and right into her lap. The furniture was full of them and they soon ate their way out into the open and stayed there, sticking clammily to the tattered blue velvet.

The foreman squatted apologetically before Helen when he arrived to take the living-room set to the dump. But when it came to it, he couldn't bear to dump the beautiful *Orang America's* things, so he took them home with him. And because his house wasn't large enough to hold them he put them out in the yard. He and his family proudly sat on Helen's wedding gifts even after the worms had finished their work and left only the bare springs and frames.

So Helen got rattan furniture that raised welts on your back. Also, her upholstered bedsteads had to be replaced by iron ones with mosquito net frames.

The dining-room furniture did not have to be disposed of. After John had spent a Sunday with a blowtorch, removing the varnish, it was all right. Then Gee could get the plates off the table without using both hands. And Helen and John could get their elbows off without leaving behind a piece of skin.

Everyone was terribly sorry about Helen's lovely things. When Mevrouw Aken saw the foreman's family sitting on the rusty springs of the living-room set, she said she could cry.

By the time the rains began to lessen in the spring, everyone felt more or less like crying. But all things come to an end, even the Java rainy monsoon. It was Mother who revived first and felt, despite her natural indolence, that she must have something to do.

Mother said later that she didn't even mention cows. All she said was how nice it would be to have some fresh milk and butter. Dad said that although she might not have mentioned cows, her remark made him think of them somehow. It made him think it would be the easiest thing in the world to have cows sent up from Australia along with some horses he was ordering.

We were all delighted with the prospect of having cows. Mother said she would learn to make butter and perhaps even cheese. Having decided to do something, she, of course, wanted to do it in a big way. The idea of cows, butter, and cheese made her feel a lot more cheerful.

Dad was feeling better too. Though no more than an additional twenty-five hundred acres had been cleared, it had looked, in midwinter, as though it would be even less than that. Now plowing and planting had begun and, best of all, the tapioca crop was flourishing and nearly ripe.

Mother wrote to Macy's for a butter churn. She knew that the buyer of the food department was not the man who sold churns but she felt he was an old friend by now. She explained that she had previously written him about exotic fruits. Unfortunately, her preserving business had failed. What she wanted now was a churn.

218

Also, if Macy's sold any of those things, whatever they were, used for making cheese, she would like one of them also, please.

Two cows and a little calf duly arrived from Australia and were put in their fine, new barn which had bars in the windows to keep wild animals out. And the bars did keep everything out but a thin, hungry, twenty-foot python. It was found one morning wrapped around the poor little calf which had been squeezed into a horrible, formless lump. After the python had been unwound and killed, the Chinese had what they liked best of all, a real, old-fashioned python dinner.

More bars were put at the windows. The cows were undisturbed now and gave plenty of milk. Though Mother's churn and cheese-making gadget had arrived, her fit of activity was past so milk was all we had. The dairyman brought it every morning and put it in the refrigerator at the inn because it was not only for us, of course, but for everyone else who wanted it.

But no one seemed to like milk except the Westlocks and ourselves. Mijnheer and Mevrouw Aken who had been born in Java, had never tasted uncanned milk. Aken said that a taste for fresh milk, like a taste for olives, must be acquired. Mijnheer De Vasca shuddered over his milk, spat it out, and called for a *pijt*.

One morning the dairyman came to the inn without his shoulder pole and buckets. He was running at full speed and trembling like a leaf. On his way from the barn *Tuan Matjan*, Lord Tiger, had suddenly appeared in his path. What could a poor *orang* do? He could only

219

crouch down and humbly beg the lord of the jungle to come kill him if he wished.

The tiger came close, so close that the man expected to feel his fangs. But instead, he heard a gulping sound and cautiously opened one eye. *Tuan Matjan* was at the bucket lapping up milk like a big pussycat. When he had finished one bucketful, he lapped up the other. Then, without a glance at the still prostrate dairyman, he loped back into the jungle.

Dad wasn't going to have his milk delivery interrupted. He would give the dairyman a rifle so he could shoot the tiger instead of offering himself for breakfast. The dairyman didn't know how to shoot and even if he did, he said, he would never dare kill *Tuan Matjan* who was not only a fearsome beast but also a powerful, malignant spirit.

One of the boar hunters was delegated to accompany the timid dairyman. But the boar hunter, when it came right down to it, felt a superstitious awe of the tiger also. When the beast appeared the hunter knelt beside the dairyman and offered himself as an additional victim. *Tuan Matjan* emptied the buckets again and loped off into the jungle.

Dad decided that the *tuans* must organize a hunt and kill the tiger. But Mijnheer Klaut suggested that they wait. We were expecting a visit from a *raden* or Javanese prince, and a visiting prince should always be given a tiger to shoot. It was the proper thing to do.

"All very well," said Mother. "But what if the tiger eats someone up in the meantime?"

30

TUAN MATJAN, Lord of the Jungle, seemed to prefer milk to meat and didn't eat anyone before the arrival of our princely visitor. The *Raden,* a very important personage in the Daringo district, was coming to attend the opening of the factory which, now that the tapioca crop was harvested, was ready to begin operations.

Opening the factory was so important that it had to be celebrated with seven whole days of *ramee-ramee* making. That meant an entire week wasted and just when the processing of the crop was supposed to start. But adat ordained it and who could refuse to conform to adat?

Klaut, never impressed with the need to hurry, said tranquilly that the situation might be much worse. It was customary in Java for all plants and factories to close down during the last two weeks of May, which, incidentally, was not harvesttime for most crops, so it was an off season on many of the plantations. During the close-down, the factories were overhauled, repaired, and cleaned. As only the coolies who did the work were busy, it meant a nice, long holiday for everyone else.

Our head foreman, Alang, had asked if our factory would be closed like all the others. Dad told him that as our brand-new, spick-and-span factory would start operations on May fifteenth, it would, of course, not be immediately closed for repairs.

Not only was the factory-opening celebration unavoidable but also the *Raden's* visit. It was the proper thing, Klaut said, to invite some important person to such festivities. Apparently it was also proper for the important person to accept, and the *Raden* would spend three days with us. Dad sighed, "Thank God it's no longer." With all the things he had on his mind, he didn't particularly want to bother with a Javanese prince.

A tiger hunt would help solve the problem of entertaining him. A public feast was planned for the first day and it would be followed by a *wayang* show. There would be a dinner the next evening and on the last night, a dance. Tiger hunting would occupy the *Raden* the rest of the time.

Everything about the *Raden's* visit had to be very special. The inn was turned over to him and his wife, *Raden Mas,* or Princess Gold, and their suite. A boat coming to Daringo from Batavia had to make a special stop down the coast to pick up the *Raden* and deposit him on our dock.

We were all there with flags and flowers to meet the prince. As soon as the gangplank was lowered a man appeared with a roll of carpeting. He gave it a push and rolled it down the gangplank to the dock. Then he himself came down, taking care not to step on the red carpet but to straddle it.

A considerable number of other people followed him.

Some of the women were so elegantly dressed that we thought one of them might be *Raden Mas* herself. But they all took care to keep one foot on each side of the thirty-inch strip of carpet. They must, we thought, be *Raden Mas's* ladies-in-waiting. It didn't occur to us that the *Raden* had brought along a flying contingent of his harem.

At last a golden umbrella was unfurled and the *Raden* himself walked down the middle of the carpet just as though he were used to it.

Like the Westlocks whom we had awaited a year before, the *Raden* looked exactly as he should. Young and slender, with regular features and large, black eyes. He wore a silk gold-embroidered sarong looped up on one side by the broad belt that held his creese. His black velvet jacket had gold braid and buttons and his turban was enormous. He was the perfect Javanese prince, Ardjuna himself, except that on top of his turban he wore a high silk hat.

Dad had taken some care in preparing his welcoming speech in Malay. Only, Mijnheer Klaut had warned him, he must not make his speech to the *Raden* himself. It was highly improper to address a prince in Malay. Dad must speak to an interpreter who would translate his speech into Krama, a special language used by an inferior when speaking to a superior or princely person.

Though the *Raden* did not speak Malay, he could understand it. But while Dad spoke he stood blank and expressionless. When the interpreter relayed the speech to him in Krama, he bowed and smiled slightly. Then the *Raden* spoke to the interpreter, not in Krama but in the special language used by a prince in speaking to an inferior. The interpreter then translated it into Malay for Dad's benefit.

The *Raden* had gone to school in Holland and had also been at Oxford. But it was not adat for him to speak or even to understand Dutch or English except on informal occasions.

The speech and reply, passing through three languages, took a very long time. The sun was blazing hot and everyone was getting tired. We were glad to see another golden umbrella unfurled. *Raden Mas* walked down the red carpet. She was muffled in a crimson silk scarf so we could only see that she was small and slender. Fortunately, no speech had been prepared for her. Without further delay she followed her husband and his umbrella bearer down the dock to the train.

Some of the flatcars had been made into passenger cars by adding wooden benches and an awning so that they looked like tiny, old-fashioned trolleys. The *Raden* sat on the front bench of the first car. His umbrella bearer sat behind him and had some difficulty in getting the golden umbrella into the space between the low awning and the high silk hat on top of the turban. *Raden Mas* took the next seat and her umbrella man sat behind her. The last bench in the car was completely occupied by a very fat man in a yellow turban.

As many of us as possible squeezed into the other two passenger cars. But the *Raden* and *Raden Mas* had

brought so many people with them that the train would have to make another trip.

Doctor Klopper told us the yellow turban showed that the fat man was an aristocrat. Gold is the symbol of princely rank and yellow denotes the noble. The fat man was a sort of prime minister and had a long and very complicated title. We couldn't remember it so we called him the Grand Vizier.

The *Raden* had just barely cracked a smile and *Raden Mas* was almost invisible in her scarf. Neither of them turned their heads to right or left during the entire ride. But the Grand Vizier kept turning in his seat to smile at us. The boys were fascinated by him and waved and smiled in return. The Grand Vizier politely waved to them but we saw that his beaming smiles were really for Helen and not for the boys.

A truck decorated with red bunting took the *Raden*, his wife, and his minister to the inn. As soon as he stepped onto the porch, the *Raden* removed his hat. He flipped the brim with his finger and it was dexterously caught by his special, royal, high-silk-hat-catcher.

31

A GIGANTIC feast was held in the village square that day. Mountains of rice were served and whole oxen were roasted on spits. All of the Javanese had a wonderful time and sat gorging themselves until late afternoon.

The *Orang Blandas* had their feast at the inn. The *Raden* was at one end of the table and *Raden Mas* at the other. The Grand Vizier was supposed to sit beside Mother, who was at the *Raden's* right, but he preferred to sit beside Helen. There was no language protocol in regard to a Grand Vizier, so he talked to her in Malay. With many flowery compliments and oily smiles, he gave Helen to understand that he greatly admired her. Unlike his master, the *Raden*, he had never been abroad and was not accustomed to *Nonya Blandas*. His admiration for Helen was for something quite new and different.

But the formality of the *Raden* and his wife was not relaxed. Each had an interpreter behind their chair and the conversation went laboriously through Malay, into Krama, then into the prince-to-an-inferior language and back into Malay.

Another difficulty was in finding something to say. After considering the weather at some length, Mother asked the interpreter how many children the *Raden* had. When the question was put to him, the *Raden* looked puzzled. He sent the interpreter to the Grand Vizier who interrupted his conversation with Helen to say that the last count brought the *Raden's* children to the number of fifty-four.

As the *Raden* had four wives and two dozen concubines, fifty-four children was really a small family. But, the interpreter said, the *Raden* was still young and would no doubt increase his family in the course of time. *Raden Mas* was the youngest and newest of his wives and she had not had any children at all as yet.

After Mother had replied rather faintly, "Fifty-four, how delightful!" she could find little else to say. Mevrouw Klaut helped the conversational ball creep along by asking how old the children were. The Grand Vizier had to be interrupted again to tell their ages. The *Raden* himself didn't pretend to keep track of their ages any more than of their number.

Dad and Mijnheer Klaut were seated beside *Raden Mas* who wore a pale green silk waist matching the green and gold of her sarong. From the jeweled pins in her hair to her little, high-heeled mules, she lived up to her name and was as exquisite as a golden doll.

In spite of her interpreter, neither Dad nor Klaut could get anything out of her but shy smiles. But she was so pretty that they were quite content just to smile back at her.

Those of us who were not seated near the princely couple didn't have to struggle to talk to them. As our lunch had not started until two o'clock we were very glad to be able to just eat and chat among ourselves.

The menu, arranged by Mevrouw Klaut, was gigantic. Besides a full European luncheon we also had a complete *rijst tafel*. When we got up from the table at four o'clock we all had to go to bed and sleep for an hour or so. By the time we were up and dressed, it was nearly time for the *wayang* to begin. So we didn't bother about dinner as we were still so full of lunch.

When we reached the market shed it was already full of people sitting on the floor or standing at the open sides. A raised platform was reserved for the *Orang Blandas*, the *Raden*, his wife, and the Grand Vizier.

At one end of the shed a stage had been built complete with footlights, curtains, and a set of scenery which was to serve for the entire show. But the *wayang* went so slowly, the plot was so complicated, and the characters so numerous, that we soon got tired of it.

All of the *Orang Javas*, however, sat as though in a trance, oblivious of time. But the *Orang Blandas* began to glance at their watches and to be sorry they had left home without having had anything to eat.

When the play finally ended at about midnight, the Javanese regretfully roused from their trance and burst into thunderous applause. We were yawning and getting up stiffly from our hard chairs when the Grand Vizier motioned us to sit down again. He had an announcement to make. A treat, a surprise was in store for us! The *Raden* had brought his troupe of dancing girls and they were going to give a performance!

Thunderous applause from the *Orang Javas* who settled back in eager anticipation. They may have been a little fatigued but they were not hungry because vendors had been supplying them with cakes and lemonade all evening.

We collapsed into our seats and tried to suppress our groans. But we *had* to have something to eat. So a boy was sent to our house to fetch sandwiches and drinks. He didn't bring quite as many sandwiches as we would have liked and they were soon gone, but there was plenty to drink: a case of soda and some whiskey as well as bottles of lemonade. All the grownups had highballs except the *Raden* and *Raden Mas*. As Mohammedans, hard liquor was forbidden them, so they joined us children in drinking lemonade. But the Grand Vizier seemed to be a renegade. He partook freely of the white man's fire water.

Not being buoyed up with whiskey, we children were pretty sleepy by that time. But we strenuously resisted Dad's suggestions that we go home to bed. I was glad we had stayed when the dancing girls or *serimpis* appeared. They were slender, golden creatures with mask-like faces under their high, jeweled tiaras. Like the *wayang* actors they moved slowly and deliberately but with the most exquisite grace.

Everyone was enthralled except Frank who dropped asleep and fell off his chair with a crash. After Dad had shaken Frank and put him back on his chair, it was Henry's turn. But he didn't crash, he subsided quietly and we didn't notice he was on the floor for some time. Then Dad, in spite of their insistence that they weren't a bit sleepy, sent them both home.

When the *serimpis*, after a final decorous bow, had left the stage, everyone applauded. The *Orang Blandas* perhaps most of all, because they had kept on with their whiskey and sodas during the performance. When the lights went up Mijnheer Klaut was very red in the face and in high spirits. The Grand Vizier was not red, but he too was in an exuberant mood which he was enjoying and wished to prolong. He didn't want the gathering to break up. So he motioned everyone to sit down and rose to announce that another treat and surprise was in store for us. He himself would take the stage and perform a dance!

His dance was in the same style as that of the *serimpis* but a fat old man going through the stately gestures was quite different from the reed-slim young girls. Too, the Grand Vizier was not quite steady on his feet but his performance was also greeted with applause by the Javanese.

The *Orang Blandas* applauded too. It seemed the polite thing to do, for one thing. For another, they were in a mood to applaud anything. Perhaps the drinks had affected the women as well as the men because Helen now said she wanted to do something. She couldn't think just what she wanted to do until she remembered her dancing class at Vassar.

When she said she wanted to dance, the Grand Vizier was delighted. He got up and announced that *Nonya* Westlock would do a dance of the *Orang Americas*. Mevrouw Assistant Overseer Vos, who had put a lot of soda in her whiskey, said it wouldn't be proper for Helen to dance in public. But Mijnheer Klaut, usually our authority on what one should and should not do, was redder than ever. He gave Helen a clap on the back and told her to go right ahead.

Helen went up on the stage and gave the orchestra directions to play as fast as they possibly could and they could speed up when they wanted to. Their tempo was fast enough for Helen's Highland fling, though the tune was not just what it should have been. But Helen did it very well right up through her last twirl and spin.

There was no applause from the Javanese. No one in the big shed clapped except the comparatively few *Orang Blandas*. But none of them gave it a thought that night.

Next day, Mijnheer Klaut, no longer red but rather yellow about the gills and dark under the eyes, deplored the fact that he had gotten drunk. If he and the others hadn't been tight, they would have told Helen that she should not dance before a Javanese audience. Among the *Orang Javas*, no women dance in public except *serimpis* who are concubines of the Raden.

The Javanese had been as shocked at Helen's Highland fling as if she had stripped and danced the *danse du ventre*.

"When," cried Helen, "will I learn not to do *anything*?"

32

DAD thought that the hunt should begin next day so the *Raden* would be sure of bagging the tiger. No need to worry about that, Klaut said. Everything would be arranged for the day following. He guaranteed there would be absolutely no danger of the *Raden* not getting *Tuan Matjan*.

So the only diversion was a tennis party in the afternoon. The *Raden* played an excellent game. It was quite a sight to see him teaming up with Miss Blue: she with her ruffles swooshing and he with his long, full, crimson sarong.

The *Raden* had taken off his creese and given it to his servant. The servant didn't want Frank and Henry to touch it but they insisted on seeing a real sword close to. The blade was narrow but wavy like a snake so that a single thrust would make an incision about three inches wide. Someone snatched the creese away from Frankie just as he was about to take a slice out of his little brother.

The dinner party that night was at our house and was an informal, non-adat occasion. The *Raden* dismissed his interpreter and spoke his Oxford English. But no one seemed to become more friendly with him in English than in any other language.

Apparently, the *Raden* didn't want *anyone* to become really friendly. Being our guest was just part, and a dull part, of his job as ruler of the Daringo district. He thought the whole business extremely boring. While adat had been in force, he did not show it. But now he allowed a touch of ennui to creep into his Oxford drawl.

Next morning, adat was in full force and the tiger hunt was arranged so that the *Raden* could shoot his tiger with an absolute minimum of fatigue. On the previous day a hole had been dug near the tiger's haunt in the jungle and baited with a live dog. During the night, *Tuan Matjan* had jumped in to get the dog and the heavy trap door had fallen. When the *Raden* appeared on the scene, the trap door was opened. While the tiger was scrambling out of the hole, the *Raden* bagged him with the greatest of ease.

Mijnheer Klaut had arranged for more hunting that morning. The huntsmen were taken to a jungle path where they were comfortably seated on camp stools. Beaters had been out since early morning and they drove the game toward the path where the huntsmen popped the animals without even getting up from their stools.

That, said Klaut proudly, was the European way of hunting! Dad explained that in America, it was done differently. There, the hunters went out and actually hunted their game. In fact, Dad said, that was what he thought "hunting" meant!

"Perhaps," said the *Raden*, lapsing into Oxford, "but it sounds excessively fatiguing to me."

As no one was fatigued by the European-style hunting, everyone was fresh for the dance that night. The porch and living room of the inn were hung with paper streamers and Japanese lanterns. Boy Two had been persuaded that the victrola was harmless. He stood by with his courage screwed to the sticking point and all ready to wind it up at the proper moment.

Everyone was in his best. Helen was most chic because her gown was only a little more than a year out of date.

234

Mother was over two years out of style. Mevrouw Klaut's dated from her last visit to Holland, seven years before. Mevrouws Aken and Vos represented some indeterminate period, while Miss Blue carried us back to the Victorian era in white silk with a bustle.

I was wearing my first evening gown which had been copied from one of Helen's. I thought I looked rather nice. The susceptible Grand Vizier, who so far had had

eyes for no one but Helen, seemed to think so also. While we were toasting the new factory with champagne, he stood at my side and regaled me with flowery compliments.

When our glasses were drained, Boy Two gingerly started the victrola. Dad asked *Raden Mas* to dance but she smiled shyly and shook her head. Her husband explained that a Javanese princess did not dance. It was not adat for a man other than her husband to so much as touch her hand.

But he himself conformed to European customs and took Mother as his partner. Dad chose Miss Blue, feeling perhaps that he would do his disagreeable duty first and get it over with.

The others assorted themselves, also. But it seemed that Mijnheer Vos didn't dance. In fact he seemed very bored with the festivities and sat in the corner drinking *pijts* with Mijnheer De Vasca who had, of course, appeared on the scene.

The Grand Vizier stood in open-mouthed astonishment when he saw the couples whirl away. Then he closed his mouth and smiled with delight. He glanced from me to Helen, in an obvious quandary as to which he should choose for his partner. His first love won out and he asked Helen for the dance. Mijnheer De Vasca, seeing me left high and dry, gallantly drained his *pijt* and clasped me to his mighty stomach.

As we danced I couldn't see much but De Vasca's gold watch chain. But I did glimpse the Grand Vizier who, turban and all, reached only to Helen's shoulder.

He had apparently never danced with anyone before but his enthusiasm made up for his awkwardness.

When the music began again and everyone started off with a different partner, the Grand Vizier looked inexpressibly amazed. As Dad waltzed off with Helen he was very chagrined and sat down in a huff and scratched his head.

Then he noticed that Miss Blue did not have a partner so he moved over beside her and began to talk. The next thing we knew, Miss Blue had jumped from her chair and bustled out of the room.

After the dance was over, the *Raden* took the Grand Vizier aside and appeared to be scolding him for offending Miss Blue. The Grand Vizier looked very contrite and went into a long explanation. The *Raden* smiled a little, the first time we had seen him really smile. Then he turned his back and appeared to be convulsed with laughter. Mijnheer Klaut joined them and he too began to smile, then broke into loud guffaws.

Dad had gone to look for Miss Blue who had not only quit the room but had left the inn as well. He felt she was his social responsibility and didn't want her to go home mad. But Miss Blue refused to discuss what the Grand Vizier had said to her and bustled off to bed.

As soon as Dad returned, Klaut buttonholed him and made him laugh. Then the two of them went to the other men and made them laugh too. None of the women were let in on the joke. The Grand Vizier, though he had started it, wasn't in on it either. He spent the rest of the evening in a corner with his turban pushed back and scratching his head.

Next day, Dad explained everything to Mother and she later told me all about it. It seems that the Grand Vizier had been laboring under a sad misapprehension. To a Javanese, the sight of men and women clasping each other in their arms could mean just one thing. The Grand Vizier had thought that a dance was only a prelude to real love-making later on in the evening. He had been shocked at the open immorality of the *Orang Blandas*. But since that was the way things were, he had been awfully happy to have the lovely Helen as his partner.

When different partners were chosen, he had been not only still more shocked but also considerably baffled. When his eye fell on the solitary Miss Blue, he was horrified. Did the fact that no one else had chosen her mean that she fell to his share? He had hurried to her and explained that whatever the other men were capable of, he was an old man. He just wasn't up to making love to her as well as to Helen. He was awfully sorry about it, but Miss Blue would have to excuse him.

33

THE departure of the *Raden, Raden Mas*, the Grand Vizier, and the rest of their company was formally conducted in Krama, Malay, and so on. Adat was in full force so there was no outward sign of the great relief on both sides that the visit was over.

Now work could begin. The tapioca roots, like giant sweet potatoes, lay in piles in the factory yard. Inside, the gleaming grinders were gaping to receive them. At six o'clock the whistle would blow and the Daringo Tapioca factory would start operations. How Dad longed to hear that whistle blow! It would sound over the Java jungle as a triumph of American energy and enterprise over rain, mud, slowness, inefficiency, and even adat itself.

That morning Dad rode to the factory with his eye on his watch. He had gone to a lot of trouble to show the whistle-blower how to blow the whistle and to impress on him that it must go off at six precisely by the big factory clock.

When the watch hand moved past six, Dad was annoyed because the fellow was not on the dot. By the time Dad reached the factory, it was ten past six. He resolved to give the man a good scolding. But the fellow was not there. The factory was empty except for the foreman, Alang.

Alang began hesitantly but finally managed to get out what he had to say. He explained it all at great length. It seemed that some things were adat and some things were not. Not only were ancient customs ruled by adat but also some newer ones after they had come into current and accepted use. There had been a great deal of discussion about it, Alang said, not only among the coolies and foremen but with the priest and the Headsman as well. Was the usual two-weeks closing of the factories customary enough to be adat?

It was finally agreed that it was. But Alang and some others had argued that in the case of our factory which was brand new, the case was different. Some said yes and some said no. But the general consensus was that adat was adat. New or old, our factory must subscribe to the general rule. No coolies would work that day, said Alang, or for the next two weeks.

Dad listened without a word. It was only when John came in that there was an argument with Alang about the decision. Dad did not argue. He knew it would be of no use.

He was white, under his tan, when he came back home. Mother exclaimed that it was such a pity about the delay, but Dad told her that in two weeks the tapioca roots would be entirely spoiled. No tapioca would be produced by the Daringo Tapioca Company that year.

Miss Blue asked if Dad was quite sure that the crop would spoil. But Dad had taken his hat, gone out of the house, and was riding away at a gallop. Always inclined to the gloomy side, Miss Blue said she certainly hoped he was not going to do anything rash.

We didn't know what Dad was going to do. But we knew it wouldn't be rash; it would be the sensible and reasonable thing in the circumstances. Dad rode to Wazi, the nearest place he could phone to the Batavia cable office. He sent a message to Roselawn saying that no tapioca would be sent from Daringo. He added that he would buy from Verstoffen the amount they were expecting and get it off to Pennsylvania on time. He did not add that he would process some of his own tapioca so as to have at least a sample of what the Daringo plantation and factory could produce. That would be only a handful and was not worth mentioning in a cable.

Now even before Dad returned from his day's trip to Wazi, John had had the same thought. He put it to Klaut, Aken, and Vos and they agreed that they should try to process some of the crop.

Next morning at six and without the blowing of the whistle, the three of them, John, Dad, and also Doctor Klopper were at the factory. John set up a worksheet just as though they were not only six men but the full three hundred who had been expected. He calculated the amount of roots that they could handle and found that only one of the sets of choppers, grinders, and pulverizers would need to be used.

Once the roots were loaded into the trucks which conveyed them into the factory, the process, which ended in the pulverized roots being dumped into the soaking vat, was practically automatic. One man must stay in the factory to work the machinery. As Klaut was older, John gave him the necessary instructions and assigned him to the task. The other men set to the heavy work of loading the roots.

The *Orang Javas,* at leisure, came to watch the work. They stood about the yard and commented on the way the various *tuans* went about their work. Doctor Klopper, who was regarded as rather effete because of his learned profession, showed that he could heave like a stevedore.

241

John, who had been a college athlete, kept pace with him pretty well. Dad was the next best loader, then Aken. Poor Vos was small and skinny and had a hard time of it.

The Chinese were also on holiday and they too came to watch and comment. Then, the impulse to lend a hand overpowered them and without saying anything, they set to work heaving roots.

Perhaps the *Orang Javas* had the same impulse. They were not lazy and further were men of good will. They all knew that the roots would spoil but the ultimate consequence of that, the final results, were so beyond their ken that they did not feel it a reason to violate adat.

The Mevrouws, Miss Blue, Helen, Mother, and we children came to watch also. Jim tried to help but some of the roots weighed as much as he did and he only got in the way. Helen, seeing poor Mijnheer Vos sweating and breathless, said that she was as big and strong as he was. She would be able to load roots as well as or better than he. When she suggested it to John, he said no. *Our* adat forbade women to do heavy work, no matter how urgent the need. But he did make Helen assistant switch thrower to Klaut. Miss Blue was rather miffed about it. She said that she had a wonderful mechanical sense and could learn to throw a switch as quickly as anyone.

When Dad paused to wipe his streaming brow, he pointed out to his fellow workers that this work was not necessary. The tapioca they would produce would be only a sample. But they all, having worked so long and so hard, were as anxious as Dad. They kept right on until, at the end of ten days, the roots began to soften and turn brown.

Five days later, the whistle blew at six o'clock and the three hundred coolies streamed into the factory. Dad was taking it easy that morning and was still in bed. He jumped up and went to the factory to explain. He told the coolies that the processed tapioca was in the soaking vat where it would remain for three weeks. After that, there would be the work of draining the vat and shoveling out the tapioca flour. But he said, he would need only six coolies to do that. He would not require the services of the rest of them.

Then he went off to Batavia to his old friend, Verstoffen, to ask what he could do about shipping some tapioca to the Roselawn Glue Company. Whatever Verstoffen said to him in the way of I-told-you-so, Dad did not repeat when he returned home.

After the water had been drained from the soaking vat, we went to watch the coolies shovel it into the shifter which ran it into bags. When the white bags were piled up, it looked like a lot of flour to us. But Dad said it was not enough to repay the expenses of shipping.

Miss Blue asked him if he was quite sure about that. Dad said, yes, he was. The flour would be kept and used for food. We were dismayed at the idea of eating a good-sized hill of tapioca pudding. But Dad explained that the flour was not fit for pudding until it had been further processed into pearls. Just plain flour was not generally used for food but it was pure and wholesome and there was no reason why it could not be eaten. Besides, it was not intended primarily for our own consumption. It would be doled out to the coolies who received food as part of their wages. Though, Dad added grimly, the time might come when we would be very glad to have some of it ourselves.

That, we realized, was true. The situation was now desperate. The only way for Dad to keep going was to borrow money, a lot of money and immediately. He had already started negotiations by cable while he was in Batavia. Now he was busy writing a lot of letters home.

John felt that Dad should abandon the whole thing and admit that he was licked. But of course Dad wouldn't do that because, John said, he was so stubborn. Dad had already put in such a lot of work. In carrying on, he would put in so much more. And in this crazy country, with these crazy people, what hope was there of ever bringing anything to success? Fortunately, John added, since Dad was determined to carry on, things were booming at home and he would have no difficulty about borrowing money.

Samples of the flour were taken to the laboratory for analysis which Dad, who was a chemist along with everything else, did himself. Despite all the time, money, and disappointment the little piles of flour had cost him, Dad's scientific enthusiasm bubbled over.

He had the best quality flour that had ever been produced! He said he would make it and he had. In that, at least, he had done what he had set out to do. He sent some of the flour to New York where, we learned afterward, it created a sensation in the tapioca world.

Mijnheer De Vasca, who knew flour when he saw it, agreed with Dad. Running the fine white stuff through his fingers, he said it was really Napoleonic. His own flour was as coarse as gravel in comparison. Mention of his own flour made Dad ask De Vasca how it was that his workers had not insisted on taking a holiday just after harvesttime.

"Oh," said De Vasca, "I had my plant shut down and overhauled in January because a shutdown in May interferes with my processing. I thought of mentioning the matter to you so you would not run into trouble. But somehow it slipped my mind, I just didn't get around to it. And by the way, Mijnheer Stryker, how about the Roselawn Glue Company buying some of my flour? It's of poor quality, true enough, but a bird in the hand is worth two in the bush."

34

NOTHING could have made Jim and me believe we would be sorry to finish our lessons with Miss Blue. But as we sat at the dining-room table on our last day of school, we were sorry and very sorry indeed. When we started school again next fall, we would be in Roselawn with Grandmother instead of at Daringo with Mother, Dad, and the little boys.

We thought we would be leaving in July because it would take two months to get home. As the last days of June came round, we were way down in the dumps. Mother was beginning to think about our packing and she was in the dumps too. She was inclined to agree with us that there was no need for us to go to college. But Dad was determined about it. Any day now, he would tell us that our tickets had been bought and that it was time for us to start off.

But Dad did not say a word about tickets, or anything else. He was very silent these days and seemed busier than ever, writing and receiving letters and cables. The last of the cables brought the news that explained why definite plans for Jim and me to go home had not been made.

We were all going!

Despite his desperate attempts, Dad had not been able to borrow money. All of his letters and cables had brought the same answers. Though things were booming at home, simply booming, for some reason in this summer of 1929, money seemed to be getting a little bit tight. Six months ago or even three, everyone said, he would have been glad to let Dad have the money. But now it was quite impossible.

Again white under his tan, Dad said that was the end of it—failure, complete and total failure.

He would have to give up and, tight-lipped, set about it. His lease must be turned back to the government and everything would be sold off. Mijnheer De Vasca announced that he would take over the lease and buy everything on the place. However, he didn't have sufficient capital to get the government to accept him as a lessee. Nor did he have money to pay for any equipment or material. Not just at the present time, at least.

The trucks and bulldozers and other movable material were sold, but the factory and power plant which had, of course, cost much more than anything else, did not find a purchaser. Dad had proved conclusively that modern machinery was not suitable for the production of tapioca.

Since we were going, Mother was in a hurry to get home. She hoped to be there in time for us to start school in September. But it all took a lot of time because turning the lease back to the government seemed to be almost as complicated as getting it.

Miss Blue was the first to depart. She left, telling us with evident satisfaction that now she was going to be governess to an *English* family. Mevrouw and Mijnheer Vos, true to form, went off without saying anything at all. Mevrouw Aken left in tears.

John said he was glad to be getting out of this crazy country. But he hated to tell us good-by and as to the factory, it broke his heart to just go off and leave it there to be overgrown by the jungle. Helen was sorry to leave us but glad to go home. Though she admitted that having to do without servants and using her splendid modern equipment herself did not fill her with enthusiasm, she had become accustomed to having nothing to do and it was really not bad.

Mother didn't really care where we were as long as

we were together. I suspect that if we were going literally as well as figuratively to the poorhouse, that would be her feeling. Time is long to children and Java had become home to the younger boys. Now home was a foreign country and going there in a big ship would be an adventure. Jim still thought that his desert island and animal-selling scheme would be better and felt that Dad was making a serious mistake. As for me, I loved Java, but had the notion that somewhere else would be even better.

We all looked forward to telling our friends that we had been around the world—to the very Antipodes and back. We had gone to a little, far-off spot on the globe and found it was not so small. It was as large as our own place on the globe and the people there lived in a world just as big, as busy and important to them as our world was to us.

The Klauts, proper to the very end, remained to see us off. With a trainload of Daringo folk who went along for the ride, they accompanied us down to the dock. Mijnheer Klaut made us a long farewell speech. Our good and loyal friend hoped that we would come back to Java some day. There was no reason to think that we would, but he who lived would see.

Of course Mijnheer De Vasca and an assortment of sons were there. He kissed Mother's hand hungrily and kissed mine also. He said he thought I was making a great mistake in not remaining and marrying Nico-demus. That was, if Dad could now scrape together enough money to give me a dowry. His last words to

248

Dad were that his venture had been Napoleonic in scope. Unfortunate that it had ended in a Waterloo. Also, Dad must remember that the De Vasca Tapioca Company always had supplies on hand at a low price.

Our good friends Boy One and Woman Cook had been upset to know we were returning to the land of the *Orang Americas*. Boy One asked if we wouldn't need a cook and houseboy back in Roselawn. Mother said that we certainly did. But Dad said that bringing Javanese into the United States would be too complicated and expensive to be worthwhile. Besides, Mother should remember that we were broke now.

Boy One was bitterly disappointed that he would never know the glamor, the dangers, and excitement of life in Pennsylvania. But his wife was relieved. She didn't want to go to the land of machines and magic that bit and talked. We told them good-by with real regret on both sides. Boy Two was also sorry to see us go. Because, he said, on his next job perhaps he would have to work.

Manisan had not been disturbed when she learned that we were leaving. She kept on chatting and giggling in a really heartless manner. When we were ready to tell her good-by, we discovered why. She was already on the boat waiting for us. When she discovered that we really couldn't take her, she wailed: "Ado, ado, ado!" Throwing adat to the winds, she hugged us all and said that she would never, never forget her dear little children.

Our boat pulled out into the bay which widened to

a blue expanse where the dock looked very small. The last we could clearly discern was Mijnheer De Vasca waving his broad-brimmed panama in one hand and blowing kisses with the other. Beside him stood our good old Manisan with her head down, crying.

We were still at the rail when the dock and flagpole had disappeared and the green of the jungle had become a distant blue blur. No one would know that the Daringo Tapioca plantation lay behind it.

Then Mother turned to Dad and said, "It was fun— for all of us. But you just didn't have time for tapioca!"

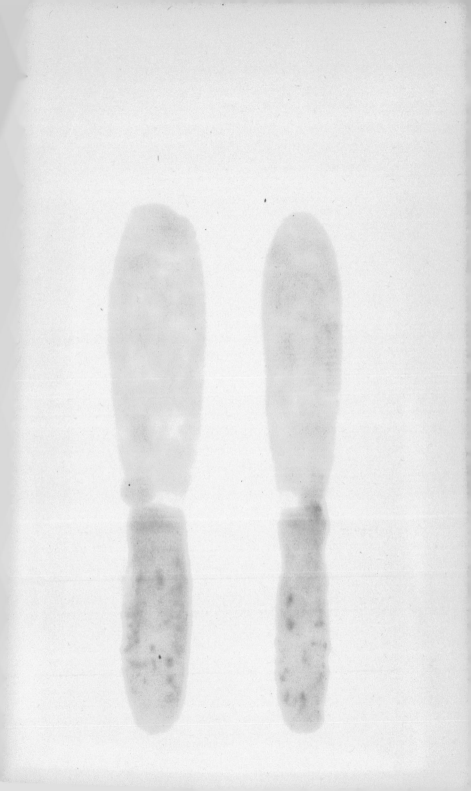